W9-ATI-550

Editor
Mary S. Jones, M.A.

Cover Artist
Barb Lorseyedi

Editor in Chief
Ina Massler Levin, M.A.

Creative Director
Karen J. Goldfluss, M.S. Ed.

Imaging
Leonard P. Swierski

Publisher
Mary D. Smith, M.S. Ed.

GRADES 5-8

TCR 2115

Coordinate GRAPHING
Creating Pictures Using Math Skills

Includes Standards & Benchmarks

- Includes practice for a wide variety of math skills
- Use as engaging independent or partner work
- Improves analytical thinking skills
- Strengthens mathematical reasoning

Teacher Created Resources

Authors
Edward M. Housel
Debra J. Housel, M.S. Ed.

Teacher Created Resources, Inc.
6421 Industry Way
Westminster, CA 92683
www.teachercreated.com

ISBN: 978-1-4206-2115-0

©2009 Teacher Created Resources, Inc.
Reprinted, 2013
Made in U.S.A.

Teacher Created Resources

Table of Contents

Introduction

Mathematics and logical thinking are the basis for science, engineering, and electronics. The ability to work with numbers and equations is a crucial part of a good education. While coordinate graphing is itself an important concept, it can also be used to reinforce a multitude of mathematical concepts in an engaging and interesting fashion.

In *Coordinate Graphing: Creating Pictures Using Math Skills* the activities and the graphs associated with each build in difficulty. Of course you do not have to do every activity in the book. Most activities reinforce concepts (such as ratio and inequalities) that you have taught using your regular math program. You can quickly glance at the Table of Contents on page 2 to find the topic you need.

Differentiate Math Instruction

The activities in this book are an excellent resource for differentiating math instruction. You can assign different activities to students at their level. An advanced student may be doing the activities on adding, subtracting, multiplying, and dividing integers, while another student is working on the activity dealing with subtracting integers. You can also pair weak students with stronger students and have them complete the graph together.

Teach About Integers

Before having students independently graph points on the coordinate plane, they need a solid knowledge of integers and the number line. Use real-life examples to help your students comprehend negative numbers. For example, you can talk about temperatures as being above zero (positive) or below zero (negative). You can also use the example of money. When you have money, that's a positive amount. When you spend more than what you have and thus owe money, it becomes a negative amount.

Explain Coordinate Graphing

Describe coordinate graphing using the appropriate terms. The *coordinate system* is a method of locating points on a plane in relation to two *perpendicular* number lines. These lines intersect at the *origin* (0,0) and divide the plane into four *quadrants*, or sections. A point is stated as an *ordered pair* (x, y). The first number in the ordered pair tells where to move horizontally along the *x axis*. If it is a positive number, move to the right. If it is a negative number, move to the left.

The second number tells where to move vertically along the *y axis*. If it is a positive number, move up the *y* axis. If it is a negative number, move down the *y* axis. Remind students that just as *x* comes before *y* in the alphabet, coordinate points are always listed in *x, y* order. The lowercase letter *y* has a tail which they can associate with the vertical axis.

In Quadrant I, both *x* and *y* have positive values. In Quadrant II, the *x* is negative and the *y* positive. In Quadrant III, both *x* and *y* have negative values, and in Quadrant IV, the *x* is positive while the *y* is negative. Graph Paper B, given on page 66 in this book, has only positive *x* and *y* values. This was done because some topics (such as negative percentages) are not taught at the grade levels for which this book is intended.

How to Use This Book

First, make one photocopy of the page you want the students to complete. Next, fold under the bottom part of the sheet (this is your answer key) prior to making the students' photocopies. The answer key also tells you the picture the students will generate by finding the values for the missing points. Make a decision as to whether or not you want to share with the students what picture the activity sheet will generate when the problems are done correctly and the points are plotted accurately.

Then make copies of the appropriate graph paper for your students. Each activity indicates which graph paper to use. There are two types of graph paper on pages 65 and 66. Graph Paper A shows the positive and negative numerical labels on the *x* and *y* axes. Graph Paper B has only one quadrant which has positive values for the *x* and *y* axes. These numbers are shown on the graph paper. This graph paper is used when an activity has a set of problems that have only positive answers. If you want to add an additional challenge, photocopy either graph paper after whiting out the numbers. Then make the students number the axes themselves.

Last, make an overhead transparency of the appropriate graph paper and display it. Do a few of the problems in the first few activities as a whole class. Then immediately plot the points. You can opt to do this with each of the activities or just in the beginning.

On page 9 there is a demonstration activity that you can do as a class or have the students do in pairs. This will ensure that they understand how to plot the points correctly.

Option: Since you may do these activities sporadically and you want the students to be as independent as possible, photocopy the Steps in Creating the Picture section (below), enlarge the text, and place it on a poster in the room.

Steps in Creating the Picture

1. Solve the problems to find the number value for each letter. If an ordered pair contains a letter, use that number to replace the letter in the ordered pair.

2. Plot the point. The first number of the coordinate pair tells how far to move horizontally from the origin (0,0). The second number of the coordinate pair tells how far to move vertically from the origin.

3. Plot the next point. Then, use a ruler to connect the two points.

4. Plot the next point and use a ruler to connect it to the one before. Continue to do this.

5. END OF LINE means that you should start a new line segment with the next ordered pair.

6. Your image should match the one given in the solutions key.

Grade 5 Standards Correlations

Each activity in this book meets at least one of the following math standards and benchmarks, which are used with permission from McREL. Copyright 2009 McREL. Mid-continent Research for Education and Learning, 4601 DTC Boulevard, Suite 500, Denver, CO 80237. Telephone: 303-337-0990. Website: *www.mcrel.org/standards-benchmarks*

Grade 5 Math Standards and Benchmarks
Standard 1. Uses a variety of strategies in the problem-solving process
6. Understands the basic language of logic in mathematical situations (e.g., "and," "or," "not") **Activity 48, 49**
Standard 2. Understands and applies basic and advanced properties of the concepts of numbers
1. Understands basic number theory concepts (e.g., prime and composite numbers, factors, multiples, odd and even numbers, divisibility) **Activity 27, 28, 29, 30**   2. Understands equivalent forms of basic percents, fractions, and decimals (e.g., 1/2 is equivalent to 50% is equivalent to 0.5) and when one form of a number might be more useful than another **Activity 37**   4. Understands the basic meaning of place value **Activity 44**   5. Understands the relative magnitude and relationships among whole numbers, fractions, decimals, and mixed numbers **Activity 31, 32, 33, 34, 35, 36, 45**
Standard 3. Uses basic and advanced procedures while performing the processes of computation
1. Multiplies and divides whole numbers **Activity 10, 11, 12**   3. Adds and subtracts simple fractions **Activity 31, 32, 35, 36**   6. Determines the effects of addition, subtraction, multiplication, and division on size and order of numbers **Activity 13, 14**   7. Understands the properties of and the relationships among addition, subtraction, multiplication, and division (e.g., reversing the order of two addends does not change the sum; division is the inverse of multiplication) **Activity 13, 14, 15, 16**   8. Solves real-world problems involving number operations (e.g., computations with dollars and cents) **Activity 45**
Standard 4. Understands and applies basic and advanced properties of the concepts of measurement
1. Understands the basic measures perimeter, area, volume, capacity, mass, angle, and circumference **Activity 50, 51**   4. Understands relationships between measures (e.g., between length, perimeter, and area) **Activity 50, 51**

Standard 5. Understands and applies basic and advanced properties of the concepts of geometry

1. Knows basic geometric language for describing and naming shapes **Activity 50, 51**

Standard 6. Understands and applies basic and advanced concepts of statistics and data analysis

1. Understands that data represent specific pieces of information about real-world objects or activities **Activity 41, 42, 43**

3. Understands that a summary of data should include where the middle is and how much spread there is around it **Activity 39, 40**

5. Reads and interprets simple bar graphs, pie charts, and line graphs **Activity 41, 42, 43**

Standard 7. Understands and applies basic and advanced concepts of probability

1. Understands that the word "chance" refers to the likelihood of an event **Activity 52, 53**

2. Recognizes events that are sure to happen, events that are sure not to happen, and events that may or may not happen **Activity 52, 53**

3. Understands that when predictions are based on what is known about the past, one must assume that conditions stay the same from the past event to the predicted future event **Activity 52, 53**

Standard 8. Understands and applies basic and advanced properties of functions and algebra

1. Recognizes a wide variety of patterns (e.g., basic linear patterns such as [2, 4, 6, 8 …]; simple repeating and growing patterns and the rules that explain them **Activity 46, 47**

3. Knows that a variable is a letter or a symbol that stands for one or more numbers **Activity 17, 18, 19, 20, 21, 22, 23, 24, 25, 26**

4. Understands the basic concept of an equality relationship (i.e., an equation is a number sentence that shows two quantities that are equal) **Activity 2, 3, 4, 5, 6, 7, 8, 54**

5. Solves simple open sentences involving operations on whole numbers (e.g., ? + 17 = 23) **Activity 17, 18, 19, 20, 21, 22, 23, 24, 25, 26, 37**

6. Knows basic characteristics and features of the rectangular coordinate system (e.g., the horizontal axis is the X axis, and the vertical axis is the Y axis) **All Activities**

Standard 9. Understands the general nature and uses of mathematics

1. Understands that numbers and the operations performed on them can be used to describe things in the real world and predict what might occur **Activity 45, 52, 53, 55, 56**

2. Understands that mathematical ideas and concepts can be represented concretely, graphically, and symbolically **Activity 52, 53, 55, 56**

Grades 6–8 Standards Correlations

Each activity in this book meets at least one of the following math standards and benchmarks, which are used with permission from McREL. Copyright 2009 McREL. Mid-continent Research for Education and Learning, 4601 DTC Boulevard, Suite 500, Denver, CO 80237. Telephone: 303-337-0990. Website: *www.mcrel.org/standards-benchmarks*

Grades 6–8 Math Standards and Benchmarks
Standard 1. Uses a variety of strategies in the problem-solving process
7. Constructs informal logical arguments to justify reasoning processes and methods of solutions to problems (i.e., uses informal deductive methods) **Activity 48, 49**
Standard 2. Understands and applies basic and advanced properties of the concepts of numbers
2. Understands the characteristics and properties (e.g., order relations, relative magnitude, base-ten place values) of the set of rational numbers and its subsets (e.g., whole numbers, fractions, decimals, integers) **Activity 44**
3. Understands the role of positive and negative integers in the number system **Activity 2, 3, 4, 5, 6, 7, 8, 9, 10, 11, 12, 13, 14, 15, 16**
4. Uses number theory concepts (e.g., divisibility and remainders, factors, multiples, prime, relatively prime) to solve problems **Activity 27, 28, 29, 30**
7. Understands the concepts of ratio, proportion, and percent and the relationships among them **Activity 37, 38**
Standard 3. Uses basic and advanced procedures while performing the processes of computation
1. Adds, subtracts, multiples, and divides integers and rational numbers **Activity 2, 3, 4, 5, 6, 7, 8, 9, 10, 11, 12, 13, 14, 15, 16**
2. Adds and subtracts fractions with unlike denominators; multiplies and divides fractions **Activity 31, 32, 33, 34, 35, 36**
5. Understands the correct order of operations for performing arithmetic computations **Activity 13, 14**
6. Uses proportional reasoning to solve mathematical and real-world problems involving equivalent fractions, equal ratios, constant rate of change, proportions, and percents **Activity 37, 38, 45**

Grades 6–8 Standards Correlations *(cont.)*

Standard 4. Understands and applies basic and advanced properties of the concepts of measurement

1. Understands the basic concept of rate as a measure (e.g., miles per gallon) **Activity 55, 56**
2. Solves problems involving perimeter (circumference) and area of various shapes (e.g. parallelograms, triangles, circles) **Activity 55, 56**
3. Understands the relationships among linear dimensions, area, and volume and the corresponding uses of units, square units, and cubic units of measure **Activity 50, 51**
7. Understands formulas for finding measure (e.g., area, volume, surface area) **Activity 50, 51**

Standard 5. Understands and applies basic and advanced properties of the concepts of geometry

2. Understands the defining properties of three-dimensional figures (e.g., a cube has edges with equal lengths, faces with equal areas and congruent shapes, right angle corners) **Activity 55, 56**

Standard 6. Understands and applies basic and advanced concepts of statistics and data analysis

1. Understands basic characteristics of measure of central tendency (i.e., mean, mode, median) **Activity 39, 40**
2. Understands basic characteristics of frequency and distribution (e.g., range, varying rates of change, gaps, clusters) **Activity 39, 40**
5. Reads and interprets simple bar graphs, pie charts, and line graphs **Activity 41, 42, 43**

Standard 7. Understands and applies basic and advanced concepts of probability

5. Understands the relationship between the numerical expression of a probability (e.g., fraction, percentage, odds) and the events that produce these numbers **Activity 52, 53**

Standard 8. Understands and applies basic and advanced properties of functions and algebra

1. Knows that an expression is a mathematical statement using numbers and symbols to represent relationships and real-world situations (e.g., equations and inequalities with or without variables) **Activity 17, 18, 19, 20, 21, 22, 23, 24, 25, 26, 54**
5. Solves linear equations using concrete, informal, and formal methods (e.g., using properties, graphing ordered pairs, using slope-intercept form) **All Activities**
6. Solves simple inequalities and non-linear equations with rational number solutions, using concrete and informal methods **Activity 54**
11. Understands the properties of arithmetic and geometric sequences (i.e., linear and exponential patterns) **Activity 46, 47**

Activity 1: Practice Plotting Points

Directions: Replace the letters in the ordered pairs below with the values given. Then plot the points on the graph paper. They will form a picture when connected in order. END OF LINE means that you should begin a new line segment with the next ordered pair.

A = ⁻8	C = 10	E = 13	G = 6	I = ⁻12
B = 1	D = 14	F = 9	H = ⁻1	J = 16

(C_____, A_____)
(B_____, J_____)
(A_____, A_____)
(D_____, G_____)
(I_____, G_____)
(C_____, A_____)
END OF LINE

(7, F_____)
(11, E_____)
END OF LINE

(⁻5, F_____)
(⁻9, E_____)
END OF LINE

(C_____, B_____)
(D_____, H_____)
END OF LINE

(B_____, ⁻6)
(B_____, ⁻10)
END OF LINE

(A_____, H_____)
(I_____, ⁻3)
END OF LINE

Activity 2: Adding Integers

Directions: Solve each problem. Use the answers to complete the ordered pairs. Then plot the points on the graph paper. They will form a picture when connected in order.

A = 5 + (‾11)	A = _____	F = 2 + (‾7)	F = _____
B = 0 + (‾9)	B = _____	G = 6 + (‾13)	G = _____
C = 4 + 9	C = _____	H = 9 + (‾20)	H = _____
D = 8 + 2	D = _____	I = 2 + 6	I = _____
E = 10 + (‾4)	E = _____	J = 3 + (‾2)	J = _____

(C_____, I_____)
(C_____, ‾8)
(11, H_____)
(‾4, H _____)
(‾4, ‾15)
(F_____, ‾12)
(G_____, H_____)
(‾8, B_____)
(A_____, G_____)
(4, G_____)
(E_____, A_____)
(E_____, J_____)
(J_____, 12)
(E_____, 9)
(5, 14)
(D_____, D_____)
(D_____, 16)
(C_____, I_____)
END OF LINE

(A_____, B_____)
(A_____, ‾10)
(F_____, ‾10)
(F_____, B_____)
(A_____, B_____)
END OF LINE

Teacher: Fold under at line before photocopying.

Activity 2 Picture: Swan

A = ‾6	C = 13	E = 6	G = ‾7	I = 8
B = ‾9	D = 10	F = ‾5	H = ‾11	J = 1

Activity 3: Adding Integers

Directions: Solve each problem. Use the answers to complete the ordered pairs. Then plot the points on the graph paper. They will form a picture when connected in order.

A = 9 + (⁻15)	A = _____	F = 8 + (⁻16)	F = _____
B = ⁻4 + 17	B = _____	G = 5 + 12	G = _____
C = ⁻7 + 2	C = _____	H = ⁻6 + 14	H = _____
D = 3 + (⁻10)	D = _____	I = ⁻4 + 0	I = _____
E = 4 + (⁻13)	E = _____	J = 5 + (⁻16)	J = _____

(B_____, B_____)   (B_____, B_____)
(B_____, 18)   (⁻1, D_____)
(H_____, G_____)   (I_____, A_____)
(9, 15)   (C_____, C_____)
(10, 14)   (A_____, ⁻3)
(B_____, B_____)   (H_____, G_____)
END OF LINE   END OF LINE

(I_____, A_____)
(C_____, D_____)
(C_____, E_____)
(A_____, E_____)
(F_____, D_____)
(F_____, A_____)
(A_____, A_____)
(C_____, C_____)
END OF LINE

(C_____, E_____)
(D_____, ⁻14)
(D_____, J_____)
(J_____, ⁻14)
(E_____, E_____)
(⁻13, ⁻10)
(F_____, A_____)
END OF LINE

- -

Teacher: Fold under at line before photocopying.

Activity 3 Picture: Rocket

A = ⁻6	C = ⁻5	E = ⁻9	G = 17	I = ⁻4
B = 13	D = ⁻7	F = ⁻8	H = 8	J = ⁻11

Activity 4: Adding Integers

Directions: Solve each problem. Use the answers to complete the ordered pairs. Then plot the points on the graph paper. They will form a picture when connected in order.

A = ⁻5 + 4	A = _____	F = 2 + 11	F = _____
B = 3 + 8	B = _____	G = 7 + 3	G = _____
C = ⁻4 + 10	C = _____	H = ⁻8 + 17	H = _____
D = ⁻11 + 16	D = _____	I = ⁻9 + 16	I = _____
E = 0 + 16	E = _____	J = ⁻5 + 8	J = _____

(H_____, E_____)
(D_____, E_____)
(D_____, D_____)
(C_____, D_____)
(C_____, F_____)
(H_____, F_____)
(H_____, E_____)
END OF LINE

(D_____, B_____)
(⁻9, B_____)
(⁻11, I_____)
(⁻12, A_____)
(G_____, A_____)
END OF LINE

(G_____, A_____)
(B_____, I_____)
(F_____, B_____)
(15, I_____)
(E_____, 0)
(G_____, A_____)
END OF LINE

(C_____, B_____)
(F_____, B_____)
END OF LINE

(⁻3, A_____)
(⁻3, ⁻18)
(J_____, ⁻18)
(J_____, A_____)
END OF LINE

(J_____, ⁻18)
(C_____, ⁻17)
(C_____, A_____)
END OF LINE

Teacher: Fold under at line before photocopying.

Activity 4 Picture: Mailbox

A = ⁻1	C = 6	E = 16	G = 10	I = 7
B = 11	D = 5	F = 13	H = 9	J = 3

Activity 5: Adding Integers

Directions: Solve each problem. Use the answers to complete the ordered pairs. Then plot the points on the graph paper. They will form a picture when connected in order.

A = ‾6 + 8	A = _____	F = 7 + (‾14)	F = _____
B = ‾3 + 18	B = _____	G = 2 + 10	G = _____
C = ‾7 + 20	C = _____	H = 5 + 4	H = _____
D = ‾1 + (‾2)	D = _____	I = 6 + 12	I = _____
E = 7 + (‾12)	E = _____	J = ‾1 + 17	J = _____

(F_____, A_____)
(B_____, A_____)
(B_____, D_____)
(F_____, D_____)
(F_____, A_____)
END OF LINE

(C_____, D_____)
(7, ‾19)
(1, ‾19)
(E_____, D_____)
END OF LINE

(C_____, A_____)
(B_____, 6)
(C_____, H_____)
(7, 11)
(1, 11)
(E_____, 8)
(F_____, 5)
(E_____, A_____)
END OF LINE

(G_____, H_____)
(B_____, G_____)
(B_____, C_____)
(C_____, J_____)
(6, I_____)
(A_____, I_____)
(‾4, J_____)
(‾6, 14)
(‾6, G_____)
(E_____, H_____)
(‾4, 8)
END OF LINE

- -

Teacher: Fold under at line before photocopying.

Activity 5 Picture: Ice Cream Cone

A = 2	C = 13	E = ‾5	G = 12	I = 18
B = 15	D = ‾3	F = ‾7	H = 9	J = 16

Activity 6: Subtracting Integers

Directions: Solve each problem. Use the answers to complete the ordered pairs. Then plot the points on the graph paper. They will form a picture when connected in order.

A = ⁻17 – (⁻5)	A = _____	F = 2 – (⁻4)	F = _____
B = 5 – (⁻2)	B = _____	G = 3 – (⁻2)	G = _____
C = 21 – 6	C = _____	H = 9 – 9	H = _____
D = 15 – 4	D = _____	I = 25 – 9	I = _____
E = 8 – 7	E = _____	J = 17 – 3	J = _____

(G_____, E_____)
(10, F_____)
(12, D_____)
(12, 13)
(D_____, C_____)
(8, I_____)
(G_____, C_____)
(2, I_____)
(⁻1, C_____)
(⁻2, 13)
(⁻2, D_____)
(H_____, F_____)
(G_____, E_____)
END OF LINE

(B_____, A_____)
(D_____, ⁻15)
(J_____, ⁻14)
(C_____, A_____)
(J_____, ⁻9)
(B_____, H_____)
(E_____, ⁻9)
(H_____, A_____)
(E_____, ⁻14)
(4, ⁻15)
(B_____, A_____)
END OF LINE

(B_____, A_____)
(8, ⁻17)
(F_____, ⁻17)
(B_____, A_____)
END OF LINE

- -

Teacher: Fold under at line before photocopying.

Activity 6 Picture: Heart and Spade

A = ⁻12	C = 15	E = 1	G = 5	I = 16
B = 7	D = 11	F = 6	H = 0	J = 14

14

Activity 7: Subtracting Integers

Directions: Solve each problem. Use the answers to complete the ordered pairs. Then plot the points on the graph paper. They will form a picture when connected in order.

A = ⁻4 – 7	A = _____	F = 3 – (⁻8)	F = _____
B = 4 – (⁻4)	B = _____	G = 13 – 8	G = _____
C = ⁻11 – (⁻3)	C = _____	H = 6 – 3	H = _____
D = 12 – 3	D = _____	I = ⁻3 – (⁻5)	I = _____
E = 24 – 11	E = _____	J = 5 – 5	J = _____

(A_____, A_____)   (⁻1, D_____)
(C_____, ⁻13)   (⁻3, B_____)
(1, ⁻14)   (⁻5, G_____)
(10, ⁻13)   (⁻7, ⁻4)
(E_____, A_____)   (⁻9, ⁻7)
(E_____, C_____)   (A_____, C_____)
(10, ⁻10)   END OF LINE
(1, A_____)
(C_____, ⁻10)   (I_____, B_____)
(A_____, C_____)   (I_____, F_____)
(A_____, A_____)   (J_____, F_____)
END OF LINE   (J_____, B_____)
          END OF LINE
(E_____, C_____)
(F_____, ⁻7)   (H_____, B_____)
(D_____, ⁻4)   (H_____, 12)
(7, G_____)   (⁻1, 12)
(G_____, B_____)   (⁻1, B_____)
(H_____, D_____)   END OF LINE
END OF LINE
          (J_____, D_____)
          (I_____, D_____)
          END OF LINE

- -

Teacher: Fold under at line before photocopying.

Activity 7 Picture: Bell

A = ⁻11	C = ⁻8	E = 13	G = 5	I = 2
B = 8	D = 9	F = 11	H = 3	J = 0

Activity 8: Subtracting Integers

Directions: Solve each problem. Use the answers to complete the ordered pairs. Then plot the points on the graph paper. They will form a picture when connected in order.

A = 0 – (⁻1)	A = _____	F = ⁻20 – (⁻4)	F = _____
B = 8 – (⁻2)	B = _____	G = 4 – (⁻9)	G = _____
C = 6 – 4	C = _____	H = 2 – 7	H = _____
D = 3 – (⁻5)	D = _____	I = ⁻15 – (⁻2)	I = _____
E = ⁻7 – (⁻10)	E = _____	J = 13 – 6	J = _____

(I_____, F_____)
(G_____, F_____)
END OF LINE

(C_____, F_____)
(C_____, A_____)
(A_____, A_____)
(A_____, F_____)
END OF LINE

(C_____, A_____)
(6, E_____)
(D_____, B_____)
(J_____, 9)
(6, B_____)
(4, D_____)
(E_____, B_____)
(A_____, J_____)
(⁻1, B_____)
(⁻2, D_____)
(H_____, B_____)
(⁻3, E_____)
(A_____, A_____)
END OF LINE

(C_____, ⁻15)
(B_____, I_____)
(G_____, ⁻8)
(G_____, H_____)
(D_____, ⁻8)
(E_____, ⁻12)
(C_____, ⁻14)
END OF LINE

(A_____, ⁻14)
(⁻6, ⁻11)
(⁻10, ⁻4)
(⁻9, ⁻1)
(H_____, ⁻3)
(0, ⁻11)
(A_____, I_____)
END OF LINE

- -

Teacher: Fold under at line before photocopying.

Activity 8 Picture: Tulip

A = 1	C = 2	E = 3	G = 13	I = ⁻13
B = 10	D = 8	F = ⁻16	H = ⁻5	J = 7

Activity 9: Multiplying Integers

Directions: Solve each problem. Use the answers to complete the ordered pairs. Then plot the points on the graph paper. They will form a picture when connected in order.

A = 2 x 0	A = _____	F = 4 x 4	F = _____
B = 6 x 1	B = _____	G = 7 x 2	G = _____
C = ⁻2 x (⁻1)	C = _____	H = 3 x 3	H = _____
D = 3 x (⁻2)	D = _____	I = ⁻4 x (⁻2)	I = _____
E = 17 x 1	E = _____	J = ⁻1 x (⁻7)	J = _____

(H_____, E_____)
(I_____, E_____)
(I_____, F_____)
(H_____, F_____)
(I_____, E_____)
END OF LINE

(3, A_____)
(C_____, ⁻4)
(3, ⁻16)
(5, ⁻17)
(C_____, ⁻17)
(1, ⁻4)
(C_____, A_____)
END OF LINE

(G_____, G_____)
(10, F_____)
END OF LINE

(1, A_____)
(⁻2, ⁻5)
(1, ⁻5)
END OF LINE

(A_____, A_____)
(⁻4, D_____)
(1, D_____)
END OF LINE

(C_____, D_____)
(B_____, D_____)
(J_____, ⁻8)
(J_____, ⁻5)
(C_____, ⁻5)
END OF LINE

(⁻12, ⁻2)
(D_____, A_____)
(B_____, A_____)
(H_____, 5)
(H_____, 15)
(10, 15)
(G_____, G_____)
(11, E_____)
(I_____, 18)
(B_____, F_____)
(B_____, J_____)
(5, B_____)
(⁻1, J_____)
(⁻8, B_____)
(⁻11, C_____)
(⁻12, ⁻2)
END OF LINE

- -

Teacher: Fold under at line before photocopying.

Activity 9 Picture: Flamingo

A = 0	C = 2	E = 17	G = 14	I = 8
B = 6	D = ⁻6	F = 16	H = 9	J = 7

Activity 10: Multiplying Integers

Directions: Solve each problem. Use the answers to complete the ordered pairs. Then plot the points on the graph paper. They will form a picture when connected in order.

A = ⁻2 x 4	A = _____	F = 6 x 1	F = _____
B = ⁻5 x (⁻1)	B = _____	G = ⁻1 x (⁻1)	G = _____
C = ⁻2 x (⁻1)	C = _____	H = ⁻3 x (⁻4)	H = _____
D = ⁻3 x 0	D = _____	I = ⁻3 x (⁻3)	I = _____
E = 5 x (⁻1)	E = _____	J = 7 x 1	J = _____

(A_____, C_____)
(⁻6, F_____)
(D_____, I_____)
(10, 3)
(14, J_____)
(H_____, G_____)
(14, ⁻3)
(I_____, D_____)
(D_____, E_____)
(⁻7, D_____)
(A_____, C_____)
END OF LINE

(D_____, I_____)
(C_____, 13)
(B_____, F_____)
END OF LINE

(E_____, B_____)
(E_____, 4)
(⁻4, 4)
(⁻4, B_____)
(E_____, B_____)
END OF LINE

(A_____, C_____)
(E_____, C_____)
END OF LINE

(B_____, G_____)
(⁻1, G_____)
(C_____, D_____)
(B_____, G_____)
END OF LINE

(A_____, F_____)
(⁻9, J_____)
(A_____, 8)
(⁻7, J_____)
(A_____, F_____)
END OF LINE

(A_____, 11)
(⁻9, H_____)
(A_____, 13)
(⁻7, H_____)
(A_____, 11)
END OF LINE

- -

Teacher: Fold under at line before photocopying.

Activity 10 Picture: Fish

A = ⁻8	C = 2	E = ⁻5	G = 1	I = 9
B = 5	D = 0	F = 6	H = 12	J = 7

Activity 11: Dividing Integers

Directions: Solve each problem. Use the answers to complete the ordered pairs. Then plot the points on the graph paper. They will form a picture when connected in order.

A = 20 ÷ 5	A = _____	F = ⁻49 ÷ (⁻7)	F = _____
B = 18 ÷ 3	B = _____	G = 121 ÷ 11	G = _____
C = 21 ÷ 7	C = _____	H = 3 ÷ 3	H = _____
D = ⁻8 ÷ (⁻4)	D = _____	I = ⁻12 ÷ 6	I = _____
E = 40 ÷ 4	E = _____	J = 36 ÷ 2	J = _____

(D_____, D_____)   (I_____, C_____)
(5, D_____)   (H_____, A_____)
(A_____, A_____)   (C_____, F_____)
(A_____, F_____)   (C_____, A_____)
(B_____, A_____)   (D_____, D_____)
(9, C_____)   END OF LINE
(12, A_____)
(13, F_____)   (B_____, I_____)
(12, E_____)   (E_____, ⁻8)
(9, G_____)   (B_____, ⁻14)
(B_____, E_____)   (D_____, ⁻8)
(A_____, 8)   (B_____, I_____)
(B_____, G_____)   END OF LINE
(F_____, 14)
(B_____, 17)
(A_____, J_____)
(C_____, J_____)
(H_____, 17)
(0, 14)
(H_____, G_____)
(C_____, 8)
(H_____, E_____)
(I_____, G_____)
(⁻5, E_____)
(⁻6, F_____)
(⁻5, A_____)

- -

Teacher: Fold under at line before photocopying.

Activity 11 Picture: Club and Diamond

A = 4	C = 3	E = 10	G = 11	I = ⁻2
B = 6	D = 2	F = 7	H = 1	J = 18

Activity 12: Dividing Integers

Directions: Solve each problem. Use the answers to complete the ordered pairs. Then plot the points on the graph paper. They will form a picture when connected in order.

A = 13 ÷ (⁻13)	A = ____	F = ⁻32 ÷ 8	F = ____
B = 10 ÷ (⁻5)	B = ____	G = 144 ÷ 12	G = ____
C = ⁻18 ÷ 3	C = ____	H = 90 ÷ 9	H = ____
D = ⁻26 ÷ (⁻13)	D = ____	I = ⁻72 ÷ (⁻9)	I = ____
E = ⁻45 ÷ 15	E = ____	J = ⁻48 ÷ 3	J = ____

(D____, ⁻5)
(A____, E____)
(F____, F____)
(C____, ⁻8)
(C____, ⁻15)
(⁻9, ⁻15)
(⁻10, J____)
(B____, J____)
(B____, ⁻8)
END OF LINE

(B____, ⁻14)
(14, J____)
(5, ⁻12)
(4, A____)
(D____, G____)
(0, 13)
(B____, G____)
(E____, H____)
(C____, 9)
(C____, I____)
(E____, 7)
(B____, 5)
(E____, 3)
END OF LINE

(F____, 1)
(⁻5, C____)
END OF LINE

(A____, D____)
(⁻9, A____)
(⁻7, D____)
(A____, 4)
END OF LINE

(C____, I____)
(F____, I____)
END OF LINE

(A____, 11)
(A____, H____)
(B____, H____)
(A____, 11)
END OF LINE

(0, 13)
(1, 15)
(D____, G____)
END OF LINE

- - - - - - - - - - - - - - - -

Teacher: Fold under at line before photocopying.

Activity 12 Picture: Kangaroo

A = ⁻1	C = ⁻6	E = ⁻3	G = 12	I = 8
B = ⁻2	D = 2	F = ⁻4	H = 10	J = ⁻16

Activity 13: Mixed Operations with Integers

Directions: Solve each problem. Use the answers to complete the ordered pairs. Then plot the points on the graph paper. They will form a picture when connected in order.

A = (5 x 6) + (⁻21)	A = _____	F = (11 x ⁻1) + 17	F = _____
B = ⁻53 + (6 x 10)	B = _____	G = (16 x 2) – 32	G = _____
C = (⁻8 x 3) + 38	C = _____	H = (7 x 6) – 45	H = _____
D = ⁻2 + (4 x 3)	D = _____	I = ⁻74 + (7 x 10)	I = _____
E = (⁻1 x 16) + 21	E = _____	J = (7 x 6) + (⁻6 x 8)	J = _____

(I_____, A_____)
(8, A_____)
(D_____, B_____)
(D_____, I_____)
(F_____, ⁻7)
(F_____, ⁻11)
(4, ⁻13)
(G_____, ⁻13)
(⁻2, ⁻11)
(⁻2, ⁻7)
(J_____, I_____)
(J_____, B_____)
(I_____, A_____)
END OF LINE

(D_____, F_____)
(13, A_____)
(C_____, C_____)
(13, 18)
(12, C_____)
(A_____, D_____)
(B_____, A _____)
END OF LINE

(J_____, F_____)
(⁻9, A_____)
(⁻10, C_____)
(⁻9, 18)
(⁻8, C_____)
(⁻5, D_____)
(H_____, A_____)
END OF LINE

(B_____, E_____)
(E_____, 3)
(4, G_____)
(B_____, 2)
(B_____, E_____)
END OF LINE

(H_____, E_____)
(H_____, 2)
(G_____, G_____)
(⁻1, 3)
(H_____, E_____)
END OF LINE

- -

Teacher: Fold under at line before photocopying.

Activity 13 Picture: Cattle Skull

A = 9	C = 14	E = 5	G = 0	I = ⁻4
B = 7	D = 10	F = 6	H = ⁻3	J = ⁻6

Activity 14: Mixed Operations with Integers

Directions: Solve each problem. Use the answers to complete the ordered pairs. Then plot the points on the graph paper. They will form a picture when connected in order.

$A = 306 + (30 \times {}^-10)$	A = _____	$F = ({}^-10 \times {}^-8) - 70$	F = _____
$B = (2 \times 6) + ({}^-7)$	B = _____	$G = (4 \times {}^-11) + 46$	G = _____
$C = ({}^-8 \times 12) + 95$	C = _____	$H = {}^-43 + (6 \times 6)$	H = _____
$D = (2 \times 5) - 2$	D = _____	$I = {}^-54 + (8 \times 5)$	I = _____
$E = ({}^-5 \times 8) + 51$	E = _____	$J = ({}^-10 \times 23) + 234$	J = _____

(B_____, B_____)
(J_____, A_____)
(B_____, 7)
(A_____, A_____)
(B_____, B_____)
END OF LINE

(E_____, A_____)
(F_____, 12)
(D_____, 16)
(B_____, 17)
END OF LINE

(A_____, D_____)
(D_____, F_____)
(B_____, 13)
END OF LINE

(B_____, J_____)
(1, 3)
(1, C_____)
(G_____, H_____)
(J_____, I_____)
(3, ⁻15)
(G_____, I_____)
(0, H_____)
(C_____, 0)
(C_____, A_____)
END OF LINE

(E_____, A_____)
(G_____, F_____)
(B_____, 13)
(B_____, 17)
(G_____, 16)
(0, 12)
(C_____, A_____)
(9, 3)
(9, C_____)
(D_____, H_____)
(A_____, I_____)
(7, ⁻15)
(D_____, I_____)
(F_____, H_____)
(E_____, C_____)
(E_____, A_____)
END OF LINE

- -

Teacher: Fold under at line before photocopying.

Activity 14 Picture: Pliers

A = 6	C = ⁻1	E = 11	G = 2	I = ⁻14
B = 5	D = 8	F = 10	H = ⁻7	J = 4

Activity 15: Review of Integer Calculations

Directions: Solve each problem. Use the answers to complete the ordered pairs. Then plot the points on the graph paper. They will form a picture when connected in order.

$A = 56 \div 7$	A = _____	$F = 19 - 7$	F = _____
$B = {}^-14 - 2$	B = _____	$G = 90 \div 10$	G = _____
$C = 11 - ({}^-4)$	C = _____	$H = 9 - 3$	H = _____
$D = {}^-12 + 12$	D = _____	$I = {}^-1 + 5$	I = _____
$E = {}^-5 - 3$	E = _____	$J = {}^-2 - ({}^-3)$	J = _____

(‾13, B_____)
(14, B_____)
END OF LINE

(E_____, C_____)
(E_____, A_____)
(‾3, H_____)
(I_____, H_____)
(G_____, A_____)
(G_____, C_____)
END OF LINE

(E_____, C_____)
(‾3, 17)
(I_____, 17)
(G_____, C_____)
(I_____, 13)
(‾3, 13)
(E_____, C_____)
END OF LINE

(E_____, A_____)
(‾12, B_____)
END OF LINE

(‾7, A_____)
(‾11, B_____)
END OF LINE

(G_____, A_____)
(13, B_____)
END OF LINE

(A_____, A_____)
(F_____, B_____)
END OF LINE

(‾9, ‾4)
(D_____, ‾6)
END OF LINE

(‾9, ‾5)
(D_____, ‾7)
END OF LINE

(J_____, ‾6)
(10, ‾4)
END OF LINE

(J_____, ‾7)
(10, ‾5)
END OF LINE

(‾4, F_____)
(‾2, A_____)
(D_____, F_____)
(2, A_____)
(I_____, F_____)
END OF LINE

(J_____, H_____)
(J_____, B_____)
END OF LINE

(D_____, H_____)
(D_____, B_____)
END OF LINE

- -

Teacher: Fold under at line before photocopying.

Activity 15 Picture: Water Tower

A = 8	C = 15	E = ‾8	G = 9	I = 4
B = ‾16	D = 0	F = 12	H = 6	J = 1

Activity 16: Review of Integer Calculations

Directions: Solve each problem. Use the answers to complete the ordered pairs. Then plot the points on the graph paper. They will form a picture when connected in order.

A = ⁻35 ÷ (⁻5)	A = _____	F = ⁻10 – (⁻4)	F = _____
B = 32 ÷ 4	B = _____	G = 11 + (⁻7)	G = _____
C = ⁻2 x (⁻3)	C = _____	H = ⁻12 – (⁻8)	H = _____
D = 7 – 2	D = _____	I = ⁻12 ÷ (⁻4)	I = _____
E = 12 – 3	E = _____	J = 0 ÷ 2	J = _____

(B_____, A_____)
(D_____, 10)
(⁻9, ⁻3)
(⁻9, F_____)
(F_____, F_____)
(B_____, A_____)
END OF LINE

(B_____, A_____)
(13, B_____)
END OF LINE

(D_____, 10)
(A_____, 16)
END OF LINE

(G_____, E_____)
(D_____, B_____)
(D_____, E_____)
(G_____, E_____)
END OF LINE

(A_____, C_____)
(C_____, A_____)
(A_____, A_____)
(A_____, C_____)
END OF LINE

(C_____, D_____)
(12, G_____)
(16, ⁻2)
(E_____, J_____)
(D_____, G_____)
END OF LINE

(E_____, J_____)
(12, ⁻7)
(C_____, H_____)
(I_____, I_____)
END OF LINE

(1, C_____)
(F_____, A_____)
(⁻10, 13)
(⁻3, 11)
END OF LINE

(2, A_____)
(⁻3, 11)
(F_____, 18)
(J_____, 15)
(I_____, B_____)
END OF LINE

(H_____, 2)
(⁻1, ⁻1)
END OF LINE

(⁻7, ⁻1)
(H_____, H_____)
END OF LINE

- -

Teacher: Fold under at line before photocopying.

Activity 16 Picture: Dragonfly

A = 7	C = 6	E = 9	G = 4	I = 3
B = 8	D = 5	F = ⁻6	H = ⁻4	J = 0

Activity 17: Addition/Subtraction with Variables

Directions: Solve each problem. Use the answers to complete the ordered pairs. Then plot the points on the graph paper. They will form a picture when connected in order.

$3 = {}^-11 + A$	$A = \rule{1cm}{0.4pt}$	$2 = 4 + F$	$F = \rule{1cm}{0.4pt}$
$2 = B - 6$	$B = \rule{1cm}{0.4pt}$	${}^-3 = 14 + G$	$G = \rule{1cm}{0.4pt}$
${}^-2 = 1 + C$	$C = \rule{1cm}{0.4pt}$	$2 = H - 4$	$H = \rule{1cm}{0.4pt}$
${}^-1 = D - 12$	$D = \rule{1cm}{0.4pt}$	${}^-1 = {}^-5 + I$	$I = \rule{1cm}{0.4pt}$
$2 = E + 2$	$E = \rule{1cm}{0.4pt}$	$3 = J + 2$	$J = \rule{1cm}{0.4pt}$

(B_____, 17)
(B_____, 5)
(D_____, H_____)
(A_____, 5)
(A_____, 3)
(D_____, I_____)
(B_____, 2)
(B_____, C_____)
(D_____, F_____)
(A_____, C_____)
(A_____, ⁻5)
(D_____, ⁻4)
(B_____, ⁻6)
(7, ⁻11)
(E_____, ⁻15)
(⁻1, G_____)
(F_____, ⁻18)
(C_____, G_____)
(C_____, ⁻15)
(I_____, ⁻10)
(I_____, ⁻8)
(E_____, E_____)
(J_____, H_____)
(H_____, D_____)
(B_____, 17)
END OF LINE

(⁻1, G_____)
(⁻1, ⁻15)
END OF LINE

(C_____, ⁻16)
(F_____, G_____)
(F_____, ⁻16)
(C_____, ⁻16)
END OF LINE

(9, ⁻5)
(A_____, ⁻6)
(A_____, ⁻8)
(10, ⁻7)
(B_____, ⁻7)
END OF LINE

(9, 3)
(A_____, 2)
(A_____, E_____)
(10, J_____)
(B_____, J_____)
END OF LINE

- -

Teacher: Fold under at line before photocopying.

Activity 17 Picture: Brontosaurus

A = 14	C = ⁻3	E = 0	G = ⁻17	I = 4
B = 8	D = 11	F = ⁻2	H = 6	J = 1

Activity 18: Addition/Subtraction with Variables

Directions: Solve each problem. Use the answers to complete the ordered pairs. Then plot the points on the graph paper. They will form a picture when connected in order.

$2 = 6 + A$	A = _____	$^-1 = F - 12$	F = _____
$^-7 = B - 1$	B = _____	$9 = 3 + G$	G = _____
$^-4 = ^-6 + C$	C = _____	$^-5 = H - 13$	H = _____
$^-5 = D + (^-4)$	D = _____	$^-3 = I - 4$	I = _____
$7 = E + 2$	E = _____	$^-2 = J + 10$	J = _____

(J_____, E_____)
(J_____, ⁻7)
(⁻10, B_____)
END OF LINE

(J_____, ⁻5)
(A_____, ⁻9)
(F_____, A_____)
END OF LINE

(A_____, ⁻11)
(A_____, I_____)
(F_____, G_____)
(F_____, B_____)
END OF LINE

(B_____, ⁻8)
(A_____, ⁻11)
(D_____, ⁻8)
END OF LINE

(H_____, ⁻5)
(F_____, B_____)
END OF LINE

(A_____, I_____)
(J_____, E_____)
(B_____, 7)
END OF LINE

(⁻10, E_____)
(A_____, C_____)
(H_____, G_____)
(C_____, 9)
END OF LINE

(F_____, G_____)
(3, 10)
(D_____, 9)
END OF LINE

(D_____, 20)
(D_____, 7)
(A_____, G_____)
(B_____, 7)
(B_____, 20)
END OF LINE

(A_____, 20)
(A_____, G_____)
END OF LINE

(D_____, B_____)
(H_____, ⁻3)
(H_____, C_____)
(E_____, C_____)
(C_____, I_____)
(D_____, D_____)
(D_____, B_____)
END OF LINE

(C_____, I_____)
(C_____, ⁻5)
END OF LINE

(E_____, C_____)
(E_____, A_____)
END OF LINE

- -

Teacher: Fold under at line before photocopying.

Activity 18 Picture: Wood Stove

A = ⁻4	C = 2	E = 5	G = 6	I = 1
B = ⁻6	D = ⁻1	F = 11	H = 8	J = ⁻12

26

Activity 19: Addition/Subtraction with Variables

Directions: Solve each problem. Use the answers to complete the ordered pairs. Then plot the points on the graph paper. They will form a picture when connected in order.

$3 = A - 4$	A = _____	$19 = F + 8$	F = _____
$4 = B - (^-2)$	B = _____	$6 = G - 2$	G = _____
$17 = C + 3$	C = _____	$3 = H + 13$	H = _____
$D - 10 = ^-5$	D = _____	$I + 16 = 4$	I = _____
$2 = E - 11$	E = _____	$J - 4 = 8$	J = _____

(B_____, H_____)   (D_____, A_____)   (J_____, F_____)
(D_____, H_____)   (10, C_____)   (10, B_____)
(D_____, A_____)   (E _____, 15)   (9, 6)
(4, G_____)   (17, E_____)   (J_____, F_____)
(3, G_____)   (J_____, ¯1)   END OF LINE
(B_____, A_____)   (C_____, ¯2)
(B_____, H_____)   (16, I_____)   (¯5, F_____)
END OF LINE   (E_____, ¯14)   (¯3, B_____)
                          (A_____, I_____)   (¯2, 6)
(B_____, A_____)   (D_____, ¯8)   (¯5, F_____)
(3, A_____)   END OF LINE   END OF LINE
END OF LINE

                          (B_____, A_____)
(D_____, A_____)   (¯3, C_____)
(4, A_____)   (¯6, 15)
END OF LINE   (H_____, E_____)
                          (¯5, ¯1)
(4, G_____)   (¯7, ¯2)
(A_____, C_____)   (¯9, I_____)
END OF LINE   (¯6, ¯14)
                          (0, I_____)
(3, G_____)   (B_____, ¯8)
(0, C_____)   END OF LINE
END OF LINE

- -

Teacher: Fold under at line before photocopying.

Activity 20 Picture: Butterfly

A = 7	C = 14	E = 13	G = 8	I = ¯12
B = 2	D = 5	F = 11	H = ¯10	J = 12

Activity 20: Addition/Subtraction with Variables

Directions: Solve each problem. Use the answers to complete the ordered pairs. Then plot the points on the graph paper. They will form a picture when connected in order.

8 = 17 – A	A = _____	F + 7 = 14	F = _____
⁻4 = ⁻8 – B	B = _____	18 + G = 20	G = _____
10 = C + 5	C = _____	2 = 15 – H	H = _____
⁻2 = 4 – D	D = _____	5 + I = 13	I = _____
⁻2 = ⁻3 – E	E = _____	7 = 11 – J	J = _____

(A_____, D_____)
(10, C_____)
(F_____, J_____)
(I_____, B_____)
(C_____, B_____)
(J_____, G_____)
(0, 1)
(B_____, G_____)
(⁻5, B_____)
(⁻8, B_____)
(⁻7, G_____)
(⁻9, E_____)
(⁻7, F_____)
(B_____, A_____)
(J_____, A_____)
(F_____, 10)
(11, A_____)
(H_____, D_____)
END OF LINE

(A_____, D_____)
(H_____, C_____)
(16, D_____)
(H_____, D_____)
(A_____, F_____)
END OF LINE

(⁻5, E_____)
(B_____, B_____)
(E_____, B_____)
(⁻3, G_____)
END OF LINE

(12, C_____)
(14, E_____)
(15, E_____)
(H_____, C_____)
END OF LINE

(A_____, A_____)
(A_____, I_____)
(10, I_____)
(A_____, A_____)
END OF LINE

(C_____, E_____)
(J_____, B_____)
(1, B_____)
(3, G_____)
END OF LINE

(D_____, A_____)
(C_____, C_____)
(I_____, D_____)
(F_____, A_____)
END OF LINE

END OF LINE

- -

Teacher: Fold under at line before photocopying.

Activity 20 Picture: Elephant

A = 9	C = 5	E = ⁻1	G = 2	I = 8
B = ⁻4	D = 6	F = 7	H = 13	J = 4

Activity 21: Multiplication with Variables

Directions: Solve each problem. Use the answers to complete the ordered pairs. Then plot the points on the graph paper. They will form a picture when connected in order.

A x 3 = 6	A = _____	0 = 2 x F	F = _____
80 = 8 x B	B = _____	3 x G = 42	G = _____
C x 3 = 33	C = _____	⁻26 = ⁻2 x H	H = _____
⁻35 = ⁻5 x D	D = _____	6 x I = 48	I = _____
⁻9 x E = ⁻45	E = _____	16 = 4 x J	J = _____

(E_____, 12)
(3, 12)
(A_____, C_____)
(A_____, A_____)
(⁻1, ⁻2)
(⁻6, ⁻3)
(⁻10, ⁻2)
(⁻12, A_____)
(⁻10, 6)
(⁻5, D_____)
(F_____, D_____)
END OF LINE

(F_____, E_____)
(⁻5, E_____)
(⁻9, J_____)
(⁻10, A_____)
(⁻9, F_____)
(⁻6, ⁻1)
(⁻2, F_____)
(F_____, A_____)
(F_____, H_____)
(A_____, G_____)
(J_____, G_____)
(E_____, H_____)
(E_____, C_____)
END OF LINE

(3, G_____)
(J_____, H_____)
(3, H_____)
(3, G_____)
END OF LINE

(A_____, D_____)
(I_____, 6)
(B_____, D_____)
(C_____, D_____)
(B_____, E_____)
(I_____, J_____)
(A_____, E_____)
END OF LINE

(B_____, D_____)
(B_____, B_____)
(C_____, B_____)
(C_____, D_____)
END OF LINE

(B_____, I_____)
(C_____, I_____)
END OF LINE

(B_____, 9)
(C_____, 9)
END OF LINE

Teacher: Fold under at line before photocopying.

Activity 21 Picture: Rattlesnake

A = 2	C = 11	E = 5	G = 14	I = 8
B = 10	D = 7	F = 0	H = 13	J = 4

Activity 22: Multiplication with Variables

Directions: Solve each problem. Use the answers to complete the ordered pairs. Then plot the points on the graph paper. They will form a picture when connected in order.

$6 = A \times (^-2)$	A = _____	$^-54 = F \times 6$	F = _____
$B \times (^-14) = ^-14$	B = _____	$77 = G \times 7$	G = _____
$^-64 = C \times 8$	C = _____	$H \times 4 = ^-16$	H = _____
$22 = D \times (^-22)$	D = _____	$^-72 = I \times 12$	I = _____
$45 = E \times (^-9)$	E = _____	$J \times (^-9) = ^-18$	J = _____

(G_____, ⁻10)
(⁻14, 6)
(⁻10, 8)
(15, C_____)
(G_____, ⁻10)
END OF LINE

(7, A_____)
(14, B_____)
(15, 6)
(12, 5)
(10, B_____)
END OF LINE

(E_____, 0)
(I_____, A_____)
(C_____, J_____)
END OF LINE

(H_____, A_____)
(I_____, A_____)
(⁻11, E_____)
END OF LINE

(H_____, A_____)
(H_____, E_____)
(D_____, ⁻2)
END OF LINE

(F_____, F_____)
(C_____, ⁻7)
(0, A_____)
END OF LINE

(G_____, 0)
(14, ⁻2)
(16, D_____)
(13, B_____)
END OF LINE

(H_____, A_____)
(A_____, D_____)
END OF LINE

(B_____, B_____)
(10, B_____)
(4, D_____)
END OF LINE

(D_____, ⁻7)
(5, I_____)
END OF LINE

(3, E_____)
(A_____, C_____)
(F_____, F_____)
(⁻11, C_____)
(⁻11, E_____)
(F_____, I_____)
(C_____, ⁻7)
END OF LINE

(9, B_____)
(7, J_____)
(9, 3)
(G_____, J_____)
END OF LINE

- -

Teacher: Fold under at line before photocopying.

Activity 22 Picture: Plane

A = ⁻3	C = ⁻8	E = ⁻5	G = 11	I = ⁻6
B = 1	D = ⁻1	F = ⁻9	H = ⁻4	J = 2

Activity 23: Division with Variables

Directions: Solve each problem. Use the answers to complete the ordered pairs. Then plot the points on the graph paper. They will form a picture when connected in order.

$3 = 15 \div A$	A = _____	$^-36 \div F = ^-3$	F = _____
$^-90 \div B = 6$	B = _____	$4 = 44 \div G$	G = _____
$4 = ^-12 \div C$	C = _____	$56 \div H = 7$	H = _____
$^-34 = ^-34 \div D$	D = _____	$^-48 \div I = ^-12$	I = _____
$^-84 \div E = 7$	E = _____	$32 = 64 \div J$	J = _____

($^-$13, B____)
(16, B____)
END OF LINE

($^-$10, B____)
($^-$10, C____)
END OF LINE

($^-$11, $^-$4)
($^-$6, I____)
(D____, 6)
(H____, I____)
(13, $^-$4)
END OF LINE

(F____, C____)
(F____, B____)
END OF LINE

($^-$1, J____)
($^-$1, C____)
(3, C____)
(3, J____)
($^-$1, J____)
END OF LINE

(D____, $^-$8)
(D____, B____)
END OF LINE

(A____, B____)
(A____, $^-$8)
(C____, $^-$8)
(C____, B____)
END OF LINE

(C____, E____)
(A____, E____)
END OF LINE

(C____, E____)
(D____, B____)
(A____, E____)
END OF LINE

(C____, B____)
(D____, E____)
(A____, B____)
END OF LINE

(13, $^-$4)
(16, $^-$2)
(G____, A____)
(A____, 7)
(D____, 6)
END OF LINE

(H____, I____)
(G____, A____)
END OF LINE

(F____, B____)
(15, $^-$13)
(15, C____)
END OF LINE

(A____, 7)
(A____, G____)
(H____, 10)
(A____, 9)
END OF LINE

- -

Teacher: Fold under at line before photocopying.

Activity 23 Picture: Barn

A = 5	C = $^-$3	E = $^-$12	G = 11	I = 4
B = $^-$15	D = 1	F = 12	H = 8	J = 2

Activity 24: Division with Variables

Directions: Solve each problem. Use the answers to complete the ordered pairs. Then plot the points on the graph paper. They will form a picture when connected in order.

$\frac{81}{A} = 9$	A= _____	$4 = \frac{56}{F}$	F = _____
$5 = \frac{B}{3}$	B= _____	$\frac{G}{2} = 5$	G = _____
$\frac{35}{C} = 7$	C= _____	$6 = \frac{48}{H}$	H = _____
$6 = \frac{24}{D}$	D= _____	$9 = \frac{63}{I}$	I = _____
$2 = \frac{E}{-7}$	E= _____	$\frac{80}{J} = {}^-8$	J = _____

(C_____, J_____)
(C_____, ⁻13)
(D_____, E_____)
(D_____, ⁻15)
(C_____, ⁻16)
(I_____, ⁻16)
(H_____, ⁻15)
(H_____, ⁻11)
END OF LINE

(A_____, ⁻11)
(D_____, J_____)
(D_____, ⁻9)
(0, ⁻5)
(⁻2, 1)
(⁻2, C_____)
(0, G_____)
(C_____, F_____)
(A_____, B_____)
(A_____, ⁻11)
END OF LINE

(A_____, F_____)
(G_____, 18)
(G_____, F_____)
(A_____, 13)
END OF LINE

(A_____, J_____)
(B_____, ⁻12)
(B_____, ⁻9)
(A_____, ⁻7)
END OF LINE

(I_____, ⁻16)
(I_____, E_____)
END OF LINE

(D_____, E_____)
(C_____, ⁻15)
(C_____, E_____)
(D_____, E_____)
END OF LINE

(A_____, ⁻4)
(B_____, ⁻3)
(B_____, ⁻6)
(A_____, ⁻7)
END OF LINE

(A_____, 12)
(B_____, F_____)
(B_____, 11)
(A_____, A_____)
END OF LINE

(A_____, A_____)
(B_____, H_____)
(B_____, C_____)
(A_____, 6)
END OF LINE

- -

Teacher: Fold under at line before photocopying.

Activity 24 Picture: Turtle

A = 9	C = 5	E = ⁻14	G = 10	I = 7
B = 15	D = 4	F = 14	H = 8	J = ⁻10

Activity 25: Multiplication/Division with Variables

Directions: Solve each problem. Use the answers to complete the ordered pairs. Then plot the points on the graph paper. They will form a picture when connected in order.

$^-20 = ^-2 \times A$	A = _____	F $\times$ 5 = 5	F = _____
$42 \div B = 3$	B = _____	$^-4 \times G = ^-48$	G = _____
$^-4 = 4 \div C$	C = _____	$0 = H \div (^-3)$	H = _____
D $\times$ 4 = 32	D = _____	$50 \div I = ^-5$	I = _____
$3 = ^-12 \div E$	E = _____	J $\times$ ($^-9$) = $^-54$	J = _____

(A_____, B_____)
(G_____, B_____)
(B_____, G_____)
(B_____, A_____)
(G_____, D_____)
(A_____, D_____)
(D_____, A_____)
(D_____, G_____)
(A_____, B_____)
END OF LINE

(A_____, E_____)
(A_____, D_____)
END OF LINE

(A_____, B_____)
(D_____, 16)
(C_____, 16)
(C_____, $^-12$)
(2, $^-18$)
END OF LINE

(C_____, 2)
(I_____, C_____)
END OF LINE

(C _____, 2)
(7, F_____)
(7, $^-2$)
(F_____, E_____)
(C_____, $^-9$)
END OF LINE

(C_____, A_____)
(I_____, A_____)
($^-9$, 9)
(C_____, 9)
END OF LINE

(J_____, E_____)
(A_____, E_____)
(13, $^-6$)
(B_____, $^-8$)
(B_____, $^-13$)
(13, $^-15$)
(A_____, $^-17$)
(J_____, $^-17$)
(3, $^-15$)
(F_____, $^-12$)
(F_____, $^-9$)
(3, $^-6$)
(J_____, E_____)
END OF LINE

(F_____, $^-12$)
(H_____, $^-14$)
(I_____, $^-14$)
(I_____, H_____)
END OF LINE

- -

Teacher: Fold under at line before photocopying.

Activity 25 Picture: Tractor

A = 10	C = $^-1$	E = $^-4$	G = 12	I = $^-10$
B = 14	D = 8	F = 1	H = 0	J = 6

Activity 26: Mixed Operations with Variables

Directions: Solve each problem. Use the answers to complete the ordered pairs. Then plot the points on the graph paper. They will form a picture when connected in order.

$1 = A - 0$	A = _____	$^-15 - F = ^-5$	F = _____
$B + (^-9) = 3$	B = _____	$^-81 = G \times (^-9)$	G = _____
$^-56 \div C = ^-7$	C = _____	$84 \div H = 6$	H = _____
$7 = D - 4$	D = _____	$35 = I \times 7$	I = _____
$^-4 + E = 2$	E = _____	$^-5 = (^-1) - J$	J = _____

(F_____, A_____)
(B_____, A_____)
END OF LINE

(F_____, A_____)
(⁻14, J_____)
(⁻6, B_____)
(A_____, H_____)
(C_____, B_____)
(16, J_____)
(B_____, A_____)
END OF LINE

(F_____, A_____)
(⁻4, D_____)
(A_____, H_____)
(E_____, D_____)
(B_____, A_____)
END OF LINE

(G_____, C_____)
(10, G_____)
(B_____, E_____)
(D_____, I_____)
(G_____, C_____)
END OF LINE

(F_____, E_____)
(⁻9, I_____)
(⁻7, C_____)
(⁻8, G_____)
(F_____, E_____)
END OF LINE

(3, A_____)
(3, C_____)
(⁻1, C_____)
(⁻1, A_____)
END OF LINE

(⁻6, B_____)
(⁻4, D_____)
(E_____, D_____)
(C_____, B_____)
END OF LINE

- -

Teacher: Fold under at line before photocopying.

Activity 26 Picture: Tent

A = 1	C = 8	E = 6	G = 9	I = 5
B = 12	D = 11	F = ⁻10	H = 14	J = 4

34

Activity 27: Prime Numbers

Directions: Circle the correct choice from the options given. Use the answers to complete the ordered pairs. Then plot the points on the graph paper. They will form a picture when connected in order.

A prime number is a whole number greater than 1 that has just two factors: 1 and itself.

A is a prime number:	A = 7	A = 4	A = 15
B is **not** a prime number:	B = 5	B =12	B = 11
C is a prime number:	C = 16	C = 33	C = 2
D is a prime number:	D = 13	D = 14	D = 18
E is **not** a prime number:	E = 17	E = 10	E = 29
F is **not** a prime number:	F = 3	F = 5	F = 9
G is **not** a prime number:	G = 19	G = 31	G = 6
H is **not** a prime number:	H =13	H = 4	H = 5
I is **not** a prime number:	I = 1	I = 23	I = 31
J is a prime number:	J = 32	J = 5	J = 8

Column 1

(14, 0)
(16, C_____)
(16, 15)
(14, 17)
END OF LINE

(D_____, 15)
(11, 17)
(A_____, 17)
(H_____, 14)
(H_____, 3)
(A_____, ⁻3)
(G_____, ⁻16)
(A_____, ⁻17)
(8, ⁻16)
(E_____, ⁻2)
(D_____, C_____)
(D_____, 15)
END OF LINE

Column 2

(D_____, D_____)
(16, 14)
END OF LINE

(D_____, H_____)
(16, 3)
END OF LINE

(H_____, F_____)
(C_____, A_____)
(C_____, I_____)
(J_____, I_____)
END OF LINE

(C_____, J_____)
(I_____, J_____)
END OF LINE

Column 3

(C_____, H_____)
(I_____, H_____)
END OF LINE

(I_____, ⁻10)
(I_____, 19)
END OF LINE

(B_____, ⁻15)
(C_____, ⁻17)
(C_____, ⁻15)
(B_____, ⁻17)
(B_____, ⁻15)
END OF LINE

(J_____, 15)
(J_____, B_____)
(8, B_____)
(11, 17)
END OF LINE

Column 4

(B_____, E_____)
(G_____, E_____)
(G_____, G_____)
(B_____, G_____)
(B_____, E_____)
END OF LINE

(A_____, F_____)
(A_____, A_____)
(F_____, A_____)
(F_____, F_____)
(A_____, F_____)
END OF LINE

(E_____, A_____)
(E_____, G_____)
END OF LINE

Teacher: Fold under at line before photocopying.

Activity 27 Picture: Helicopter

A = 7	C = 2	E = 10	G = 6	I = 1
B = 12	D = 13	F = 9	H = 4	J = 5

Activity 28: Factors

Directions: Determine the value of each variable. Use the answers to complete the ordered pairs. Then plot the points on the graph paper. They will form a picture when connected in order.

The unique factors of A are (⁻1, ⁻2, ⁻7, **A**)	A = _____
The unique factors of 18 are (1, 2, 3, 6, **B**, 18)	B = _____
The unique factors of 50 are (1, 2, 5, **C**, 25, 50)	C = _____
The unique factors of 33 are (1, 3, **D**, 33)	D = _____
The unique factors of E are (⁻1, ⁻2, ⁻3, **E**)	E = _____
The unique factors of ⁻24 are (⁻1, ⁻2, ⁻3, ⁻6, **F**, ⁻12, ⁻24)	F = _____
The unique factors of 45 are (1, 3, 5, 9, **G**, 45)	G = _____
The unique factors of 60 are (1, 2, 3, 4, 5, 6, 10, **H**, 15, 20, 30, 60)	H = _____
The unique factors of 40 are (1, 2, 4, 5, **I**, 10, 20, 40)	I = _____
The unique factors of 70 are (1, 2, 5, 7, 10, **J**, 35, 70)	J = _____

(7, ⁻9)
(6, A_____)
(5, A_____)
(5, F_____)
END OF LINE

(⁻5, F_____)
(⁻4, A_____)
(⁻3, A_____)
(⁻3, F_____)
END OF LINE

(C_____, H_____)
(D_____, H_____)
(D_____, D_____)
(C_____, D_____)
(C_____, H_____)
END OF LINE

(B_____, 13)
(B_____, J_____)
(I_____, G_____)
(I_____, J_____)
(B_____, 13)
END OF LINE

(G_____, C_____)
(H_____, C_____)
END OF LINE

(⁻13, A_____)
(J_____, A_____)
END OF LINE

(B_____, E_____)
(D_____, B_____)
(G_____, C_____)
(G_____, D_____)
(B_____, 13)
(7, C_____)
(I_____, B_____)
(6, ⁻2)
(E_____, ⁻3)
(F_____, E_____)
(⁻7, ⁻7)
(E_____, ⁻5)
(⁻7, A_____)
(E_____, A_____)
(⁻5, F_____)
(7, F_____)
(I_____, A_____)
(B_____, A_____)
(B_____, E_____)
END OF LINE

Teacher: Fold under at line before photocopying.

Activity 28 Picture: Giraffe

A = ⁻14	C = 10	E = ⁻6	G = 15	I = 8
B = 9	D = 11	F = ⁻8	H = 12	J = 14

Activity 29: Factors

Directions: Determine the value of each variable. Use the answers to complete the ordered pairs. Then plot the points on the graph paper. They will form a picture when connected in order.

The unique factors of 20 are (1, 2, **A**, 5, 10, 20)	A = _____
The unique factors of 42 are (1, 2, 3, 6, 7, **B**, 21, 42)	B = _____
The unique factors of 75 are (1, 3, 5, **C**, 25, 75)	C = _____
The unique factors of 36 are (1, 2, 3, 4, 6, 9, **D**, 18, 36)	D = _____
The unique factors of 27 are (1, 3, **E**, 27)	E = _____
The unique factors of 12 are (1, **F**, 3, 4, 6, 12)	F = _____
The unique factors of 39 are (1, 3, **G**, 39)	G = _____
The unique factors of 55 are (1, 5, **H**, 55)	H = _____
The unique factors of 30 are (1, 2, 3, 5, 6, **I**, 15, 30)	I = _____
The unique factors of J are (1, 2, 4, **J**)	J = _____

(F_____, J_____)
(A_____, 3)
(‾2, 5)
END OF LINE

(1, D_____)
(‾7, H_____)
(‾3, J_____)
END OF LINE

(A_____, B_____)
(A_____, G_____)
(5, G_____)
(5, B_____)
END OF LINE

(J_____, G_____)
(J_____, D_____)
(E_____, D_____)
END OF LINE

(C_____, I_____)
(H_____, I_____)
END OF LINE

(5, C_____)
(7, 18)
END OF LINE

(A_____, C_____)
(A_____, 19)
END OF LINE

(3, C_____)
(F_____, 18)
END OF LINE

(0, A_____)
(‾2, F_____)
(‾5, ‾4)
(‾6, ‾9)
(‾4, ‾14)
(‾8, ‾12)
(‾12, ‾14)
(‾9, ‾7)
(‾7, A_____)
(‾4, E_____)
END OF LINE

(F_____, 7)
(B_____, E_____)
(C_____, I_____)
(B_____, H_____)
(I_____, H_____)
(E_____, D_____)
(E_____, G_____)
(6, B_____)
(F_____, B_____)
(‾1, D_____)
END OF LINE

- -

Teacher: Fold under at line before photocopying.

Activity 29 Picture: Dolphin

A = 4	C = 15	E = 9	G = 13	I = 10
B = 14	D = 12	F = 2	H = 11	J = 8

Activity 30: Greatest Common Factor

Directions: Determine the value of each variable. Use the answers to complete the ordered pairs. Then plot the points on the graph paper. They will form a picture when connected in order.

A is the greatest common factor of 30 and 50	A = _____
B is the greatest common factor of 9 and 15	B = _____
C is the greatest common factor of 36 and 54	C = _____
D is the greatest common factor of 39 and 65	D = _____
E is the greatest common factor of 27 and 45	E = _____
F is the greatest common factor of 6 and 10	F = _____
G is the greatest common factor of 45 and 75	G = _____
H is the greatest common factor of 33 and 55	H = _____
I is the greatest common factor of 21 and 35	I = _____
J is the greatest common factor of 48 and 80	J = _____

(F_____, C_____)	(B_____, C_____)	(I_____, E_____)
(1, G_____)	(I_____, J_____)	(I_____, ⁻3)
(1, D_____)	(12, J_____)	(6, ⁻4)
(F_____, A_____)	(G_____, 14)	(6, ⁻18)
(B_____, D_____)	(J_____, H_____)	(8, ⁻19)
(B_____, G_____)	(14, D_____)	(E_____, ⁻19)
(F_____, C_____)	(12, 14)	(H_____, ⁻18)
END OF LINE	(H_____, D_____)	(H_____, ⁻4)
	(A_____, E_____)	(A_____, ⁻3)
(F_____, C_____)	(I_____, E_____)	(A_____, E_____)
(B_____, C_____)	(6, 12)	END OF LINE
(4, G_____)	(B_____, A_____)	
(4, D_____)	END OF LINE	
(B_____, A_____)		
(F_____, A_____)		
END OF LINE		

- -

Teacher: Fold under at line before photocopying.

Activity 30 Picture: Hammer

A = 10	C = 18	E = 9	G = 15	I = 7
B = 3	D = 13	F = 2	H = 11	J = 16

Activity 31: Adding Fractions

Directions: Solve each problem. Use the answers to complete the ordered pairs. Then plot the points on the graph paper. They will form a picture when connected in order.

$A = 7\frac{2}{7} + \frac{5}{7}$ A = _____ $F = 12\frac{3}{8} + \frac{5}{8}$ F = _____

$B = \frac{14}{22} + 5\frac{4}{11}$ B = _____ $G = \frac{6}{10} + \frac{32}{5}$ G = _____

$C = \frac{6}{10} + \frac{22}{5}$ C = _____ $H = \frac{16}{7} + \frac{5}{7}$ H = _____

$D = (^{-}\frac{9}{7}) + (^{-}\frac{5}{7})$ D = _____ $I = (^{-}\frac{6}{10}) + (^{-}\frac{22}{5})$ I = _____

$E = \frac{1}{3} + \frac{2}{3}$ E = _____ $J = 8\frac{4}{9} + \frac{5}{9}$ J = _____

(J_____, H_____)   (H_____, A_____)   (E_____, D_____)
(B_____, A_____)   (C_____, F_____)   (⁻1, ⁻7)
(D_____, A_____)   (J_____, 17)   (I_____, ⁻11)
(I_____, H_____)   END OF LINE   END OF LINE
(D_____, D_____)
(B_____, D_____)   (E_____, A_____)   (⁻1, D_____)
(J_____, H_____)   (⁻1, F_____)   (⁻3, I_____)
END OF LINE   (I_____, 17)   (⁻8, ⁻7)
                                END OF LINE   END OF LINE

(A_____, E_____)
(10, 0)   (⁻1, A_____)   (B_____, B_____)
(12, E_____)   (⁻3, 11)   (G_____, C_____)
(A_____, 2)   (⁻8, F_____)   (B_____, C_____)
END OF LINE   END OF LINE   (B_____, B_____)
                                                                END OF LINE

(A_____, 4)   (C_____, D_____)
(12, C_____)   (G_____, I_____)   (G_____, E_____)
(10, B_____)   (F_____, ⁻7)   (B_____, 0)
(A_____, C_____)   END OF LINE   (B_____, E_____)
END OF LINE   (G_____, E_____)
                                (H_____, D_____)   END OF LINE
(C_____, A_____)   (C_____, ⁻7)
(G_____, 11)   (J_____, ⁻11)
(F_____, F_____)   END OF LINE
END OF LINE

- -

Teacher: Fold under at line before photocopying.

Activity 31 Picture: Spider

A = 8   C = 5   E = 1   G = 7   I = ⁻5

B = 6   D = ⁻2   F = 13   H = 3   J = 9

Activity 32: Subtracting Fractions

Directions: Solve each problem. Use the answers to complete the ordered pairs. Then plot the points on the graph paper. They will form a picture when connected in order.

$A = \frac{33}{7} - \frac{5}{7}$	A = _____	$F = \frac{37}{13} - \frac{11}{13}$	F = _____
$B = 10\frac{4}{11} - (\frac{-14}{22})$	B = _____	$G = \frac{12}{7} - \frac{5}{7}$	G = _____
$C = \frac{47}{7} - \frac{5}{7}$	C = _____	$H = (\frac{-1}{4}) - (\frac{-2}{8})$	H = _____
$D = 8\frac{5}{9} - \frac{5}{9}$	D = _____	$I = 15\frac{5}{16} - \frac{10}{32}$	I = _____
$E = 12\frac{2}{5} - (\frac{-3}{5})$	E = _____	$J = 9\frac{1}{2} - (\frac{-2}{4})$	J = _____

(B_____, ⁻19)
(B_____, 19)
END OF LINE

(B_____, I_____)
(A_____, 19)
(A_____, J_____)
(C_____, D_____)
(C_____, ⁻10)
(B_____, ⁻10)
END OF LINE

(A_____, 16)
(F_____, I_____)
(G_____, I_____)
(G_____, 7)
(C_____, 5)
END OF LINE

(F_____, I_____)
(F_____, E_____)
(A_____, E_____)
END OF LINE

(A_____, B_____)
(F_____, B_____)
(F_____, D_____)
(A_____, D_____)
(A_____, J_____)
END OF LINE

(G_____, D_____)
(⁻8, 7)
END OF LINE

(H_____, E_____)
(H_____, J_____)
(⁻1, J_____)
(⁻1, E_____)
(H_____, E_____)
END OF LINE

(H_____, 12)
(G_____, 12)
END OF LINE

(H_____, B_____)
(G_____, B_____)
END OF LINE

(C_____, ⁻9)
(⁻3, ⁻15)
(C_____, ⁻8)
END OF LINE

(C_____, ⁻6)
(5, ⁻7)
(A_____, ⁻7)
(3, ⁻6)
(3, ⁻5)
(A_____, ⁻4)
(5, ⁻4)
(C_____, ⁻5)
END OF LINE

(3, ⁻5)
(⁻3, ⁻15)
(D_____, ⁻15)
(D_____, ⁻16)
(7, ⁻16)
END OF LINE

- -

Teacher: Fold under at line before photocopying.

Activity 32 Picture: Fishing Trawler

A = 4	C = 6	E = 13	G = 1	I = 15
B = 11	D = 8	F = 2	H = 0	J = 10

Activity 33: Multiplying Fractions

Directions: Solve each problem. Use the answers to complete the ordered pairs. Then plot the points on the graph paper. They will form a picture when connected in order.

$A = \frac{8}{2} \times (\frac{-3}{2})$	A = _____	$F = \frac{5}{2} \times (\frac{-8}{4})$	F = _____
$B = \frac{18}{3} \times (\frac{-2}{3})$	B = _____	$G = (\frac{-6}{3}) \times \frac{7}{2}$	G = _____
$C = (\frac{-1}{2}) \times (\frac{-32}{4})$	C = _____	$H = (\frac{-7}{4}) \times (\frac{-8}{2})$	H = _____
$D = \frac{9}{3} \times \frac{3}{3}$	D = _____	$I = \frac{20}{5} \times (\frac{-1}{4})$	I = _____
$E = \frac{2}{4} \times \frac{12}{3}$	E = _____	$J = \frac{15}{5} \times \frac{13}{3}$	J = _____

(H_____, E_____)
(E_____, ‾3)
(H_____, A_____)
(6, G_____)
(I_____, B_____)
(I_____, ‾2)
(C_____, D_____)
END OF LINE

(‾2, D_____)
(‾8, 0)
(A_____, B_____)
(G_____, F_____)
(‾11, 0)
(‾10, E_____)
(F_____, 5)
END OF LINE

(1, 0)
(B_____, E_____)
END OF LINE

(C_____, I_____)
(J_____, I_____)
(15, E_____)
(J_____, C_____)
(11, C_____)
(10, D_____)
(9, D_____)
(‾3, H_____)
(B_____, 12)
(‾10, 16)
(‾11, 16)
(‾10, 14)
(A_____, 10)
(A_____, C_____)
END OF LINE

(12, C_____)
(11, D_____)
(12, E_____)
(J_____, D_____)
(12, C_____)
END OF LINE

(J_____, I_____)
(11, 0)
END OF LINE

(9, F_____)
(H_____, A_____)
(9, A_____)
END OF LINE

(8, G_____)
(6, G_____)
(H_____, ‾8)
END OF LINE

(B_____, B_____)
(A_____, B_____)
(B_____, F_____)
END OF LINE

(F_____, A_____)
(G_____, F_____)
(A_____, G_____)
END OF LINE

- -

Teacher: Fold under at line before photocopying.

Activity 33 Picture: Salamander

A = ‾6	C = 4	E = 2	G = ‾7	I = ‾1
B = ‾4	D = 3	F = ‾5	H = 7	J = 13

Activity 34: Dividing Fractions

Directions: Solve each problem. Use the answers to complete the ordered pairs. Then plot the points on the graph paper. They will form a picture when connected in order.

$A = \frac{1}{2} \div \frac{1}{14}$	A = _____	$F = (\frac{-12}{3}) \div \frac{2}{4}$	F = _____
$B = (\frac{-3}{4}) \div (\frac{-3}{8})$	B = _____	$G = (\frac{-3}{2}) \div (\frac{-1}{10})$	G = _____
$C = \frac{3}{2} \div \frac{1}{6}$	C = _____	$H = \frac{21}{3} \div \frac{1}{2}$	H = _____
$D = (\frac{-5}{5}) \div \frac{3}{3}$	D = _____	$I = \frac{1}{2} \div (\frac{-1}{6})$	I = _____
$E = (\frac{-3}{3}) \div \frac{1}{2}$	E = _____	$J = (\frac{-7}{7}) \div (\frac{-1}{6})$	J = _____

(G_____, 20)
(G_____, ⁻20)
END OF LINE

(G_____, G_____)
(H_____, 16)
(C_____, 18)
(4, 16)
(B_____, H_____)
(J_____, 12)
(A_____, C_____)
(A_____, ⁻10)
(J_____, ⁻13)
(B_____, ⁻15)
(4, ⁻17)
(C_____, ⁻19)
(H_____, ⁻17)
(G_____, ⁻16)
END OF LINE

(D_____, A_____)
(1, D_____)
(D_____, D_____)
(I_____, A_____)
END OF LINE

(⁻7, A_____)
(C_____, A_____)
(10, J_____)
(H_____, J_____)
(H_____, C_____)
(10, C_____)
(C_____, 8)
(⁻7, 8)
(⁻7, A_____)
END OF LINE

(A_____, B_____)
(0, B_____)
END OF LINE

(E_____, B_____)
(I_____, B_____)
(⁻4, 0)
(I_____, E_____)
(A_____, E_____)
END OF LINE

(I_____, D_____)
(⁻5, D_____)
(⁻6, E_____)
(F_____, E_____)
END OF LINE

(I_____, 1)
(⁻5, 1)
(⁻5, B_____)
(F_____, B_____)
END OF LINE

(F_____, 4)
(F_____, ⁻4)
END OF LINE

(F_____, B_____)
(⁻10, 1)
(⁻10, D_____)
(F_____, E_____)
END OF LINE

Teacher: Fold under at line before photocopying.

Activity 34 Picture: Canoe

A = 7	C = 9	E = ⁻2	G = 15	I = ⁻3
B = 2	D = ⁻1	F = ⁻8	H = 14	J = 6

Activity 35: Mixed Operations with Fractions

Directions: Solve each problem. Use the answers to complete the ordered pairs. Then plot the points on the graph paper. They will form a picture when connected in order.

$A = (\frac{-3}{2}) \div (\frac{-3}{8})$ A = _____ $F = (\frac{-3}{4}) \times (\frac{-12}{3})$ F = _____

$B = (\frac{-6}{10}) - 13\frac{2}{5}$ B = _____ $G = 2 \div (\frac{-2}{5})$ G = _____

$C = \frac{3}{4} \times 8$ C = _____ $H = (^-6\frac{2}{7}) - \frac{5}{7}$ H = _____

$D = (^-2\frac{5}{9}) + (\frac{-4}{9})$ D = _____ $I = (\frac{-40}{5}) \times \frac{5}{4}$ I = _____

$E = 2 \div \frac{1}{5}$ E = _____ $J = (^-10\frac{1}{3}) - \frac{2}{3}$ J = _____

(7, I_____)   (G_____, A_____)   (E_____, 11)
(C_____, ⁻12)   (B_____, 0)   (C_____, 11)
(8, B_____)   (H_____, 9)   END OF LINE
(2, B_____)   (⁻4, E_____)
(A_____, ⁻12)   (⁻4, 13)   (C_____, B_____)
(A_____, J_____)   (D_____, 16)   (C_____, ⁻13)
END OF LINE   (0, 18)   END OF LINE
                     (1, 18)
(D_____, J_____)   (A_____, 16)   (A_____, B_____)
(D_____, ⁻12)   (5, 13)   (A_____, ⁻13)
(⁻1, B_____)   (E_____, 11)   END OF LINE
(H_____, B_____)   (C_____, E_____)
(G_____, ⁻12)   (9, 9)   (D_____, B_____)
(⁻6, I_____)   (16, 0)   (D_____, ⁻13)
END OF LINE   (C_____, A_____)   END OF LINE
                     END OF LINE
(H_____, F_____)   (G_____, B_____)
(H_____, ⁻2)   (A_____, 15)   (G_____, ⁻13)
(⁻6, I_____)   (F_____, 15)   END OF LINE
(⁻4, J_____)   (F_____, 14)
(5, J_____)   (A_____, 14)
(7, I_____)   (A_____, 15)
(8, ⁻2)   END OF LINE
(8, F_____)
END OF LINE

- -

Teacher: Fold under at line before photocopying.

Activity 35 Picture: Penguin

A = 4   C = 6   E = 10   G = ⁻5   I = ⁻10

B = ⁻14   D = ⁻3   F = 3   H = ⁻7   J = ⁻11

Activity 36: Mixed Operations with Fractions

Directions: Solve each problem. Use the answers to complete the ordered pairs. Then plot the points on the graph paper. They will form a picture when connected in order.

$A = \frac{6}{10} - \frac{3}{5}$	A = _____	$F = (^-\frac{3}{4}) \div (^-\frac{3}{16})$	F = _____
$B = \frac{12}{3} \times \frac{7}{4}$	B = _____	$G = \frac{9}{3} \div \frac{9}{9}$	G = _____
$C = (^-\frac{8}{5}) + \frac{6}{10}$	C = _____	$H = (^-\frac{4}{4}) \div (^-\frac{6}{6})$	H = _____
$D = 5\frac{2}{5} - (^-\frac{6}{10})$	D = _____	$I = 9\frac{2}{7} + \frac{5}{7}$	I = _____
$E = \frac{2}{4} \times 16$	E = _____	$J = (^-\frac{3}{2}) \times (^-6)$	J = _____

(C_____, D_____)
(H_____, E_____)
(A_____, 12)
(⁻3, 14)
(⁻7, 13)
(⁻8, J_____)
(⁻5, D_____)
(C_____, D_____)
END OF LINE

(C_____, D_____)
(A_____, G_____)
(G_____, 2)
(5, F_____)
(F_____, B_____)
(H_____, E_____)
END OF LINE

(G_____, 2)
(F_____, C_____)
(B_____, ⁻2)
(J_____, A_____)
(E_____, G_____)
(5, F_____)
END OF LINE

(13, H_____)
(11, H_____)
(J_____, A_____)
(I_____, C_____)
END OF LINE

(B_____, ⁻6)
(D_____, ⁻4)
(B_____, ⁻2)
(E_____, ⁻3)
END OF LINE

(5, F_____)
(B_____, B_____)
(11, B_____)
END OF LINE

(G_____, 2)
(A_____, C_____)
(A_____, ⁻5)
END OF LINE

(A_____, G_____)
(⁻3, A_____)
(⁻3, ⁻4)
END OF LINE

(C_____, D_____)
(⁻5, F_____)
(⁻6, A_____)
END OF LINE

(H_____, E_____)
(2, 12)
(B_____, 12)
END OF LINE

(F_____, B_____)
(D_____, I_____)
(I_____, I_____)
END OF LINE

(D_____, C_____)
(B_____, C_____)
END OF LINE

(E_____, A_____)
(E_____, H_____)
END OF LINE

- -

Teacher: Fold under at line before photocopying.

Activity 36 Picture: Ant

A = 0	C = ⁻1	E = 8	G = 3	I = 10
B = 7	D = 6	F = 4	H = 1	J = 9

Activity 37: Percents

Directions: Solve each problem. Use the answers to complete the ordered pairs. Then plot the points on the graph paper. They will form a picture when connected in order.

52% = A ÷ 25	A = _____	100% = 4 ÷ F	F = _____
40% = 2 ÷ B	B = _____	2% = G ÷ 50	G = _____
0.11 = C%	C = _____	48% = H ÷ 25	H = _____
16% = D ÷ 50	D = _____	40% = 4 ÷ I	I = _____
6% = E ÷ 100	E = _____	0.09 = J%	J = _____

(14, A_____)
(I_____, A_____)
(D_____, H_____)
(7, H_____)
(⁻2, D_____)
(⁻4, B_____)
(0, G_____)
END OF LINE

(C_____, G_____)
(A_____, 2)
END OF LINE

(J_____, D_____)
(E_____, B_____)
(E_____, F_____)
(J_____, G_____)
(A_____, G_____)
END OF LINE

(F_____, ⁻4)
(G_____, ⁻3)
(F_____, ⁻3)
END OF LINE

(3, 2)
(E_____, F_____)
END OF LINE

(I_____, A_____)
(C_____, H_____)
(I_____, H_____)
(I_____, A_____)
END OF LINE

(0, 7)
(B_____, I_____)
(D_____, C_____)
END OF LINE

(D_____, B_____)
(A_____, B_____)
END OF LINE

(C_____, B_____)
(A_____, E_____)
END OF LINE

(C_____, B_____)
(I_____, E_____)
(J_____, E_____)
END OF LINE

(C_____, G_____)
(D_____, F_____)
(D_____, B_____)
(H_____, J_____)
(14, A_____)
(H_____, C_____)
END OF LINE

(⁻1, E_____)
(3, 2)
(3, 0)
(2, ⁻2)
(G_____, ⁻3)
(⁻5, 3)
(⁻5, F_____)
(⁻3, F_____)
END OF LINE

- -

Teacher: Fold under at line before photocopying.

Activity 37 Picture: Frog

A = 13	C = 11	E = 6	G = 1	I = 10
B = 5	D = 8	F = 4	H = 12	J = 9

Activity 38: Ratio and Proportion

Directions: Determine the value of each variable. Use the answers to complete the ordered pairs. Then plot the points on the graph paper. They will form a picture when connected in order.

⁻24 : **A** = 9 : 3	A = _____	**F** : 60 = 2 : 8	F = _____
⁻3 : **B** = 4 : 8	B = _____	2 : 1 = **G** : 2	G = _____
⁻44 : **C** = 12 : 3	C = _____	**H** : ⁻1.5 = 32 : 16	H = _____
5 : 1 = **D** : 2	D = _____	**I** : 48 = 2 : 6	I = _____
E : ⁻6 = 3 : 9	E = _____	0 : 19 = **J** : 38	J = _____

(A_____, B_____)
(A_____, ⁻17)
(D_____, ⁻17)
(D_____, B_____)
(A_____, B_____)
END OF LINE

(A_____, B_____)
(⁻5, H_____)
(⁻1, ⁻4)
(3, ⁻4)
(7, H_____)
(D_____, B_____)
END OF LINE

(⁻5, H_____)
(⁻7, 1)
(A_____, I_____)
(E_____, F_____)
(G_____, F_____)
(D_____, I_____)
(9, 1)
(7, H_____)
END OF LINE

(G_____, J_____)
(G_____, 14)
END OF LINE

(D_____, 13)
(13, 11)
(13, 5)
(9, 3)
END OF LINE

(9, 1)
(F_____, 5)
(F_____, 12)
(D_____, F_____)
END OF LINE

(E_____, A_____)
(E_____, C_____)
(J_____, C_____)
(J_____, A_____)
(E_____, A_____)
END OF LINE

(2, A_____)
(2, C_____)
(G_____, C_____)
(G_____, A_____)
(2, A_____)
END OF LINE

(6, A_____)
(6, C_____)
(8, C_____)
(8, A_____)
(6, A_____)
END OF LINE

(B_____, A_____)
(B_____, C_____)
(⁻4, C_____)
(⁻4, A_____)
(B_____, A_____)
END OF LINE

(A_____, I_____)
(H_____, 17)
(5, 17)
(D_____, I_____)
END OF LINE

(E_____, 14)
(E_____, J_____)
END OF LINE

Teacher: Fold under at line before photocopying.

Activity 38 Picture: Blender

A = ⁻8	C = ⁻11	E = ⁻2	G = 4	I = 16
B = ⁻6	D = 10	F = 15	H = ⁻3	J = 0

Activity 39: Mean/Average

Directions: Determine the value of each variable. Use the answers to complete the ordered pairs. Then plot the points on the graph paper. They will form a picture when connected in order.

A = mean of (⁻11, ⁻12, ⁻13, ⁻8)	A = _____
B = mean of (⁻9, ⁻6, ⁻11, ⁻14, ⁻10)	B = _____
C = mean of (⁻9, ⁻13, ⁻10, ⁻12, ⁻16)	C = _____
D = mean of (⁻2, 2, ⁻1, 0, 6)	D = _____
E = mean of (⁻2, 4, 2, 1, ⁻5)	E = _____
F = mean of (⁻7, ⁻9, ⁻3, ⁻11, ⁻5)	F = _____
G = mean of (12, 9, 8, 13, 13)	G = _____
H = mean of (⁻6, ⁻4, ⁻7, ⁻12, ⁻11)	H = _____
I = mean of (9, 7, 4, 6, 4)	I = _____
J = mean of (4, 6, ⁻1, ⁻1)	J = _____

(C_____, A_____)
(16, A_____)
(15, C_____)
(C_____, C_____)
(C_____, A_____)
END OF LINE

(12, C_____)
(10, ⁻15)
(A_____, ⁻15)
(C_____, C_____)
END OF LINE

(J_____, F_____)
(D_____, H_____)
END OF LINE

(⁻6, A_____)
(⁻5, ⁻9)
(I_____, ⁻9)
(8, A_____)
END OF LINE

(⁻5, ⁻9)
(⁻5, H_____)
(I_____, H_____)
(I_____, ⁻9)
END OF LINE

(⁻4, A_____)
(⁻4, B_____)
(⁻3, B_____)
(⁻3, A_____)
END OF LINE

(D_____, A_____)
(D_____, B_____)
(J_____, B_____)
(J_____, A_____)
END OF LINE

(⁻1, A_____)
(⁻1, B_____)
(E_____, B_____)
(E_____, A_____)
END OF LINE

(4, A_____)
(4, B_____)
(5, B_____)
(5, A_____)
END OF LINE

(D_____, H_____)
(D_____, G_____)
(E_____, G_____)
(E_____, H_____)
END OF LINE

(D_____, G_____)
(16, A_____)
(I_____, F_____)
(J_____, F_____)
(D_____, G_____)
END OF LINE

(E_____, F_____)
(B_____, F_____)
(B_____, ⁻6)
(E_____, ⁻6)
END OF LINE

(B_____, ⁻6)
(E_____, G_____)
END OF LINE

(B_____, F_____)
(C_____, A_____)
END OF LINE

- -

Teacher: Fold under at line before photocopying.

Activity 39 Picture: Sailboat

A = ⁻11	C = ⁻12	E = 0	G = 11	I = 6
B = ⁻10	D = 1	F = ⁻7	H = ⁻8	J = 2

Activity 40: Mode

Directions: Determine the value of each variable. Use the answers to complete the ordered pairs. Then plot the points on the graph paper. They will form a picture when connected in order.

A = mode of (‾14, ‾12, ‾10, ‾9, ‾10, ‾17)   A = _____

B = mode of (‾18, ‾13, ‾16, ‾22, ‾23, ‾16, ‾14)   B = _____

C = mode of (13, 6, 12, 18, 12, 14)   C = _____

D = mode of (10, 14, 10, 6, 17, 10, 5)   D = _____

E = mode of (4, 15, 9, 13, 9, 7)   E = _____

F = mode of (15, 20, 10, 15, 15, 19)   F = _____

G = mode of (6, 13, 18, 13, 19, 9)   G = _____

H = mode of (2, 5, 4, 7, 2, 2, 9)   H = _____

I = mode of (14, 8, 14, 13, 14, 19, 21)   I = _____

J = mode of (13, 11, 12, 11, 10, 11, 5)   J = _____

(F_____, G_____)	(G_____, E_____)	(F_____, G_____)	(3, ‾15)
(C_____, I_____)	(C_____, C_____)	(C_____, G_____)	(H_____, B_____)
(D_____, 18)	(F_____, G_____)	END OF LINE	(3, ‾17)
(D_____, 16)	END OF LINE		END OF LINE
(E_____, 18)		(J_____, I_____)	
(E_____, 16)	(5, A_____)	(D_____, F_____)	(H_____, B_____)
(7, 18)	(4, ‾12)	(D_____, I_____)	(4, B_____)
(E_____, D_____)	(5, B_____)	(J_____, I_____)	END OF LINE
(7, ‾1)	(4, ‾15)	END OF LINE	
(0, ‾1)	(3, ‾12)		
(‾2, E_____)	(4, A_____)	(3, A_____)	
(‾7, C_____)	END OF LINE	(H_____, ‾12)	
(A_____, C_____)		(H_____, B_____)	
(‾9, J_____)	(6, ‾15)	(1, ‾15)	
(‾11, J_____)	(5, B_____)	(1, ‾12)	
(‾9, D_____)	(6, ‾17)	(H_____, A_____)	
(A_____, E_____)	END OF LINE	END OF LINE	
(‾6, ‾7)			
(‾1, A_____)	(5, B_____)		
(8, A_____)	(7, B_____)		
(F_____, ‾3)	END OF LINE		

- -

Teacher: Fold under at line before photocopying.

Activity 40 Picture: Rooster

A = ‾10	C = 12	E = 9	G = 13	I = 14
B = ‾16	D = 10	F = 15	H = 2	J = 11

Activity 41: Interpreting a Bar Graph

Directions: Use the graph to determine the value of each variable. Use the values to complete the ordered pairs. Then plot the points on the graph paper. They will form a picture when connected in order.

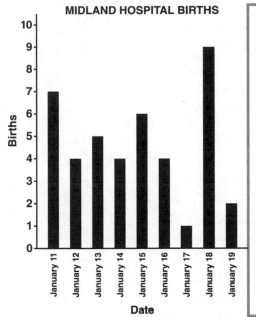

A = sum of the number of babies born on January 11, 12, 13, and 19

   A = _____

B = sum of the number of babies born on January 11, 12, 13, 15, 17, and 18

   B = _____

C = sum of the number of babies born on January 11, 12, and 15

   C = _____

D = sum of the number of babies born January 11, 12, 15, and 16

   D = _____

E = sum of the number of babies born January 11–13

   E = _____

F = most babies born on a single date between January 11 and January 17

   F = _____

G = sum of the number of babies born January 11, 13, 15, 18

   G = _____

H = sum of the number of babies born January 11, 12, 13 and 15

   H = _____

I = average number of babies born daily January 11–January 16

   I = _____

J = mode for babies born daily January 11–January 19

   J = _____

(H_____, B_____) (A_____, B_____) (6, D_____) (9, A_____)
(H_____, 39) (J_____, D_____) (12, D_____) (F_____, E_____)
(A_____, 35) (2, C_____) (19, G_____) (F_____, C_____)
(C_____, 28) (2, 14) (13, G_____) (8, A_____)
(H_____, B_____) (J_____, 13) (6, D_____) (9, A_____)
END OF LINE (F_____, 14) END OF LINE END OF LINE
  (20, 24)

(12, G_____) (25, 31) (F_____, C_____) (8, 20)
(13, 30) END OF LINE (I_____, C_____) (6, A_____)
(15, B_____)   (I_____, E_____) END OF LINE
(A_____, B_____) (H_____, B_____) (F_____, E_____)
END OF LINE (24, B_____) END OF LINE
  (25, 31)

(E_____, G_____) (31, 30) (I_____, C_____)
(9, D_____) (28, 26) (J_____, A_____)
END OF LINE (20, 24) (J_____, C_____)
  END OF LINE (I_____, E_____)
    END OF LINE

- -

Teacher: Fold under at line before photocopying.

Activity 41 Picture: Space Shuttle

| A = 18 | C = 17 | E = 16 | G = 27 | I = 5 |
| B = 32 | D = 21 | F = 7 | H = 22 | J = 4 |

Activity 42: Interpreting a Bar Graph

Directions: Use the graph to determine the value of each variable. Use the values to complete the ordered pairs. Then plot the points on the graph paper. They will form a picture when connected in order.

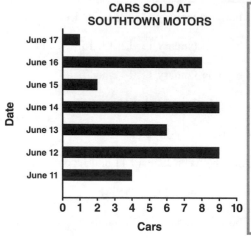

CARS SOLD AT SOUTHTOWN MOTORS

A = sum of cars sold on June 14 and 15   A = _____

B = sum of cars sold June 11–June 15   B = _____

C = sum of cars sold on June 11, 12, and 14   C = _____

D = mode of cars sold June 11–June 17   D = _____

E = sum of cars sold on June 12, 14, and 15   E = _____

F = sum of cars sold on June 11 and June 12   F = _____

G = median for car sales on June 11, 13, 14, and 16   G = _____

H = sum of cars sold June 11–June 16   H = _____

I = sum of cars sold on June 11, 12, 15, and 17   I = _____

J = sum of cars sold on June 11, 12, and 17   J = _____

(C_____, H_____)
(B_____, B_____)
(C_____, I_____)
(J_____, B_____)
(C_____, H_____)
END OF LINE

(C_____, H_____)
(C_____, I_____)
END OF LINE

(J_____, B_____)
(B_____, B_____)
END OF LINE

(C_____, B_____)
(27, 10)
(B_____, 5)
(32, 3)
END OF LINE

(C_____, I_____)
(E_____, A_____)
(J_____, D_____)
(D_____, 10)
END OF LINE

(E_____, A_____)
(C_____, D_____)
(21, 8)
(E_____, A_____)
END OF LINE

(E_____, A_____)
(19, F_____)
(17, F_____)
(E_____, A_____)
END OF LINE

(F_____, A_____)
(15, G_____)
(F_____, G_____)
(15, A_____)
(F_____, A_____)
END OF LINE

(D_____, 12)
(D_____, G_____)
(G_____, 8)
(A_____, 12)
(D_____, 12)
END OF LINE

Teacher: Fold under at line before photocopying.

Activity 42 Picture: Kite

A = 11   C = 22   E = 20   G = 7   I = 16

B = 30   D = 9   F = 13   H = 38   J = 14

Activity 43: Interpreting a Line Graph

Directions: Use the graph to determine the value of each variable. Use the values to complete the ordered pairs. Then plot the points on the graph paper. They will form a picture when connected in order.

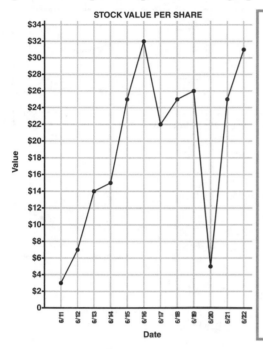

A = stock value mean for June 11 through June 13   A = _____

B = stock value mode for the days listed   B = _____

C = stock value on June 13   C = _____

D = maximum stock value   D = _____

E = stock value on June 17   E = _____

F = stock value on June 22   F = _____

G = stock value on June 19   G = _____

H = stock value on June 14   H = _____

I = stock value on June 12   I = _____

J = stock value on June 20   J = _____

(B_____, A_____)   (A_____, A_____)   (E_____, B_____)   (C_____, D_____)
(4, A_____)   (A_____, B_____)   (E_____, A_____)   (C_____, F_____)
(J_____, I_____)   END OF LINE   END OF LINE   END OF LINE
(J_____, 2)
(B_____, 2)   (E_____, B_____)   (C_____, D_____)   (H_____, D_____)
(B_____, A_____)   (A_____, B_____)   (H_____, D_____)   (H_____, F_____)
END OF LINE   (I_____, G_____)   (17, 34)   END OF LINE
                       (I_____, 30)   (17, 36)

(B_____, 6)   (A_____, F_____)   (C_____, 39)
(G_____, 3)   (E_____, F_____)   (C_____, 37)
(28, J_____)   (23, 30)   (12, 34)
(28, 10)   (23, G_____)   (C_____, D_____)
(G_____, 11)   (E_____, B_____)   END OF LINE
(B_____, A_____)   END OF LINE
END OF LINE

- -

Teacher: Fold under at line before photocopying.

Activity 43 Picture: Candle

A = 8	C = 14	E = 22	G = 26	I = 7
B = 25	D = 32	F = 31	H = 15	J = 5

Activity 44: Rounding and Absolute Value

Directions: Determine the value of each variable. Use the answers to complete the ordered pairs. Then plot the points on the graph paper. They will form a picture when connected in order.

A = absolute value of ⁻7	A = _____
582,400 rounded to the nearest thousand = 58**B**,000	B = _____
13,940 rounded to the nearest hundred = 13,**C**00	C = _____
5,464 rounded to the nearest ten = 5,4**D**0	D = _____
E = absolute value of ⁻5	E = _____
F = ⁻0.6 rounded to the nearest integer	F = _____
G = ⁻2.2 rounded to the nearest integer	G = _____
H = 8.43 rounded to the nearest whole number	H = _____
370 rounded to the nearest hundred = **I**00	I = _____
925 rounded to the nearest ten = 9**J**0	J = _____

(F_____, ⁻6)
(⁻5, ⁻6)
(⁻9, ⁻4)
(⁻12, 13)
(⁻11, 14)
(⁻6, 14)
(⁻3, C_____)
(⁻4, G_____)
(⁻3, B_____)
(F_____, D_____)
(I_____, H_____)
(D_____, 12)
(A_____, H_____)
(C_____, D_____)
(C_____, E_____)
(E_____, I_____)
END OF LINE

(B_____, E_____)
(A_____, J_____)
(C_____, J_____)
(H_____, B_____)
END OF LINE

(C_____, B_____)
(A_____, B_____)
(B_____, I_____)
END OF LINE

(G_____, G_____)
(0, F_____)
(B_____, G_____)
(B_____, ⁻7)
(J_____, ⁻8)
(F_____, ⁻8)
(F_____, ⁻4)
END OF LINE

(I_____, J_____)
(B_____, G_____)
END OF LINE

(C_____, E_____)
(A_____, E_____)
END OF LINE

(A_____, A_____)
(D_____, H_____)
(D_____, A_____)
(A_____, A_____)
END OF LINE

- -

Teacher: Fold under at line before photocopying.

Activity 44 Picture: Squirrel

A = 7	C = 9	E = 5	G = ⁻2	I = 4
B = 2	D = 6	F = ⁻1	H = 8	J = 3

Activity 45: Money

Directions: Solve each problem. Use the answers to complete the ordered pairs. Then plot the points on the graph paper. They will form a picture when connected in order.

A¢ = the sum of 2 dimes and 3 pennies	A = _____
$B = $4 + $16	B = _____
C¢ = the sum of 1 dime, 1 nickel, and 2 pennies	C = _____
D¢ = the change when a purchase costs $11.76 and $12 is given to the cashier	D = _____
$E = $30 − $2	E = _____
$F = the total of a twenty-dollar bill, a five-dollar bill, and a one-dollar bill	F = _____
$G = the change from a $79 purchase when a one hundred-dollar bill is used to pay	G = _____
$H = $200 − $186	H = _____
$I = the total of two five-dollar bills	I = _____
J¢ = $0.20 − $0.16	J = _____

(E_____, J_____)   (1, 30)   (A_____, C_____)   (D_____, 34)
(E_____, G_____)   (G_____, 7)   (18, C_____)   (A_____, 32)
(F_____, A_____)   (22, 8)   (18, H_____)   (E_____, 35)
(D_____, G_____)   (G_____, I_____)   (A_____, H_____)   (F_____, 40)
(D_____, J_____)   (J_____, 29)   END OF LINE   (B_____, 39)
(F_____, 2)   END OF LINE   (25, 33)
(E_____, J_____)   (12, F_____)   END OF LINE
END OF LINE   (B_____, 39)   (I_____, 22)
          (1, 30)   (8, 22)   (18, 16)
(A_____, A_____)   (J_____, 29)   (7, D_____)   (H_____, 16)
(A_____, 2)   (B_____, 37)   (9, 29)   (H_____, 15)
(C_____, 2)   (G_____, 38)   (12, F_____)   (18, 15)
(C_____, B_____)   END OF LINE   END OF LINE   END OF LINE
(B_____, A_____)
(A_____, A_____)   (C_____, 19)   (11, 27)   (A_____, I_____)
END OF LINE   (B_____, 19)   (H_____, 35)   (D_____, I_____)
          (B_____, A_____)   (13, 35)   END OF LINE
(C_____, 6)   END OF LINE   (I_____, E_____)
(12, 6)   END OF LINE   (A_____, 15)
(13, 5)   (D_____, 15)
(C_____, 5)   END OF LINE
END OF LINE

--- --- --- --- --- --- --- --- --- --- --- --- --- --- --- --- --- --- --- ---

Teacher: Fold under at line before photocopying.

Activity 45 Picture: Power Shovel

A = 23	C = 17	E = 28	G = 21	I = 10
B = 20	D = 24	F = 26	H = 14	J = 4

Activity 46: Sequences

Directions: Complete the sequences by determining the missing numbers. Use the answers to complete the ordered pairs. Then plot the points on the graph paper. They will form a picture when connected in order.

(12, **F**, 2, ⁻3, **E**, ⁻13, ⁻18, ⁻23)   F = _____, E = _____

(3, 7, **B**, 15, 19, 23)   B = _____

(12, 9, **G**, 3, **I**, **J**, ⁻6, **D**, ⁻12, ⁻15, ⁻18)   G = _____, I = _____, J = _____, D = _____

(4, 6, **C**, 10, 12, 14)   C = _____

(2.5, **H**, **A**, 20, 40, 80, 160)   H = _____, A = _____

(H_____, C_____)   (A_____, A_____)   (B_____, D_____)   (G_____, D_____)
(G_____, F_____)   (A_____, B_____)   (B_____, E_____)   (F_____, ⁻10)
(H_____, 3)   (B_____, A_____)   (12, D_____)   END OF LINE
(D_____, J_____)   (A_____, A_____)   END OF LINE
(2, C_____)   END OF LINE
(H_____, C_____)   (16, ⁻6)
END OF LINE   (F_____, I_____)   (B_____, E_____)
                     (F_____, J_____)   (A_____, E_____)
(2, C_____)   (A_____, E_____)   (F_____, D_____)
(C_____, B_____)   (A_____, D_____)   (G_____, D_____)
(B_____, B_____)   END OF LINE   (⁻11, ⁻13)
(12, A_____)   END OF LINE
(16, 9)
(12, C_____)   (C_____, I_____)   (C_____, ⁻10)
(B_____, 2)   (C_____, J_____)   (F_____, D_____)
(9, I_____)   (B_____, E_____)   (H_____, J_____)
(⁻7, ⁻2)   END OF LINE   (G_____, I_____)
END OF LINE   END OF LINE
                     (16, E_____)
                     (A_____, ⁻10)
(E_____, ⁻2)   (⁻11, ⁻15)   (H_____, I_____)
(⁻13, ⁻2)   END OF LINE   (4, J_____)
(⁻12, 3)   (G_____, D_____)
(E_____, 2)   (G_____, ⁻10)
(⁻1, H_____)   END OF LINE
END OF LINE

- -

Teacher: Fold under at line before photocopying.

Activity 46 Picture: Robin

| A = 10 | C = 8 | E = ⁻8 | G = 6 | I = 0 |
| B = 11 | D = ⁻9 | F = 7 | H = 5 | J = ⁻3 |

Activity 47: Sequences

Directions: Complete the sequences by determining the missing numbers. Use the answers to complete the ordered pairs. Then plot the points on the graph paper. They will form a picture when connected in order.

(1, **G**, 9, 16, 25, 36, 49, 64, 81, 100, 121, 144)	G = _____
(1.5, **B**, **E**, **D**, 24, 48, 96, 192)	B = _____, E = _____, D = _____
(15, **F**, 7, 3, ⁻1, **I**, **C**, ⁻13, ⁻17, ⁻21)	F = _____, I = _____, C = _____
(16, **J**, 12, 10, 8, 6, 4, 2, 0, **H**, ⁻4, ⁻6, **A**, ⁻10, ⁻12, ⁻14)	J = _____, H = _____, A = _____

(I_____, E_____)
(H_____, J_____)
(1, 16)
(G_____, 16)
(7, J_____)
(7, D_____)
END OF LINE

(5, D_____)
(7, D_____)
(10, F_____)
(F_____, 9)
(9, 8)
(G_____, 8)
END OF LINE

(F_____, 9)
(8, 9)
(5, 10)
END OF LINE

(5, 8)
(5, E_____)
(E_____, B_____)
(E_____, A_____)
(B_____, ⁻17)
END OF LINE

(⁻3, A_____)
(H_____, C_____)
(⁻1, A_____)
(1, B_____)
(H_____, E_____)
(I_____, E_____)
(A_____, G_____)
(⁻13, ⁻14)
(⁻12, ⁻17)
(C_____, ⁻15)
(⁻7, C_____)
END OF LINE

(C_____, ⁻15)
(A_____, ⁻18)
(I_____, ⁻16)
(H_____, C_____)
END OF LINE

(H_____, ⁻4)
(⁻3, A_____)
(I_____, C_____)
(⁻6, A_____)
(I_____, ⁻4)
END OF LINE

(⁻6, A_____)
(⁻7, C_____)
(A_____, A_____)
(⁻7, ⁻4)
END OF LINE

(B_____, J_____)
(2, 13)
(B_____, D_____)
(G_____, 13)
(B_____, J_____)
END OF LINE

(1, D_____)
(2, F_____)
(B_____, F_____)
(G_____, D_____)
END OF LINE

- -

Teacher: Fold under at line before photocopying.

Activity 47 Picture: Eagle

A = ⁻8	C = ⁻9	E = 6	G = 4	I = ⁻5
B = 3	D = 12	F = 11	H = ⁻2	J = 14

Activity 48: Logic

Directions: Determine the value of each variable. Use the answers to complete the ordered pairs. Then plot the points on the graph paper. They will form a picture when connected in order.

Set 1 = {14, 1, ⁻14, 5}	**Set 2** = {0, 4, 7, 14}	**Set 3** = {4, 5, ⁻13, 3}	**Set 4** = {⁻14, ⁻13, 2, 0}
A is only in Set 1	A = ____	F is in both Set 2 and Set 3	F = ____
B is only in Set 2	B = ____	G is in both Set 3 and Set 4	G = ____
C is only in Set 3	C = ____	H is in both Set 1 and Set 3	H = ____
D is only in Set 4	D = ____	I is in both Set 1 and Set 4	I = ____
E is in both Set 1 and Set 2	E = ____	J is in both Set 2 and Set 4	J = ____

(E____, 18) (8, G____) (6, H____) (D____, ⁻15)
(E____, ⁻19) (8, I____) (F____, A____) (F____, I____)
END OF LINE END OF LINE (C____, A____) (D____, I____)
                                                  (H____, H____) END OF LINE

(E____, ⁻15) (10, G____) END OF LINE
(13, ⁻19) (10, I____)   (C____, D____)
END OF LINE END OF LINE (B____, H____) (A____, D____)
                                               (F____, H____) (J____, A____)

(E____, 10) (B____, 9) END OF LINE (A____, J____)
(B____, 19) (A____, H____)   (C____, J____)
(B____, G____) (A____, F____) (B____, ⁻1) END OF LINE
(E____, G____) (B____, F____) (C____, ⁻1)
END OF LINE END OF LINE (C____, ⁻2)
                                               (B____, ⁻3)

(E____, ⁻15) (B____, D____) END OF LINE
(B____, ⁻15) (C____, D____)
(6, ⁻16) (C____, J____) (D____, ⁻12)
(A____, ⁻16) (B____, J____) (D____, G____)
(A____, ⁻11) END OF LINE (F____, G____)
(6, ⁻11)   (F____, ⁻12)
(6, I____) (A____, C____) (C____, ⁻12)
(E____, I____) (A____, ⁻1) (C____, G____)
END OF LINE END OF LINE END OF LINE

- -

Teacher: Fold under at line before photocopying.

Activity 48 Picture: Motorboat

A = 1	C = 3	E = 14	G = ⁻13	I = ⁻14
B = 7	D = 2	F = 4	H = 5	J = 0

Activity 49: Logic

Directions: Determine the value of each variable. Use the answers to complete the ordered pairs. Then plot the points on the graph paper. They will form a picture when connected in order.

Set 1 = {‾5, 12, ‾2, 3}	Set 2 = {12, ‾4, ‾3, 2}	Set 3 = {0, ‾3, ‾5, 11}	Set 4 = {‾4, 3, 11, ‾1}
A is only in Set 1	A = _____	F is in both Set 2 and Set 3	F = _____
B is only in Set 2	B = _____	G is in both Set 3 and Set 4	G = _____
C is only in Set 3	C = _____	H is in both Set 1 and Set 3	H = _____
D is only in Set 4	D = _____	I is in both Set 1 and Set 4	I = _____
E is in both Set 1 and Set 2	E = _____	J is in both Set 2 and Set 4	J = _____

(E_____, J_____)   (C_____, B_____)   (C_____, A_____)   (D_____, A_____)
(G_____, F_____)   (C_____, 4)   (C_____, J_____)   (D_____, D_____)
(E_____, A_____)   (H_____, 5)   (H_____, J_____)   (A_____, D_____)
END OF LINE   (H_____, 6)   (H_____, H_____)   (D_____, A_____)
                         (J_____, 7)   (J_____, ‾6)   END OF LINE
(E_____, B_____)   (J_____, E_____)   (F_____, ‾13)
(G_____, I_____)   (C_____, 19)   (1, ‾18)   (G_____, F_____)
(E_____, 4)   (D_____, 14)   (C_____, ‾14)   (A_____, A_____)
END OF LINE   (1, E_____)   (B_____, ‾11)   (F_____, C_____)
                         (D_____, 9)   (C_____, ‾8)   (A_____, B_____)
(G_____, F_____)   (I_____, 6)   (I_____, ‾6)   (G_____, I_____)
(E_____, F_____)   (B_____, B_____)   (B_____, A_____)   (10, C_____)
END OF LINE   END OF LINE   END OF LINE   (G_____, F_____)
                                                                          END OF LINE
(G_____, I_____)   (D_____, B_____)
(E_____, I_____)   (D_____, 1)
END OF LINE   (A_____, 1)
                                                  (D_____, B_____)
(A_____, A_____)   END OF LINE
(H_____, A_____)
(F_____, C_____)
(H_____, B_____)
(A_____, B_____)
END OF LINE

- -

Teacher: Fold under at line before photocopying.

Activity 49 Picture: Bat

A = ‾2	C = 0	E = 12	G = 11	I = 3
B = 2	D = ‾1	F = ‾3	H = ‾5	J = ‾4

Activity 50: Geometry

Directions: Solve each problem. Use the answers to complete the ordered pairs. Then plot the points on the graph paper. They will form a picture when connected in order.

A box's volume is 144 in.³. It has sides of 3 in., 3 in., and **A** in.	A = _____
A triangle has a base of 11 cm and a height of 6 cm. Its area is **B** cm².	B = _____
A quadrilateral has sides of 8 cm, 9 cm, 5 cm, and 7 cm. Its perimeter is **C** cm.	C = _____
A square has a perimeter of 76 in. **D** is the length of one of its sides.	D = _____
A rectangle has sides of 7 ft. and 2 ft. Its area is **E** ft.².	E = _____
A cube has a volume of 52 cm³ and sides of 2 cm, 2 cm, and **F** cm.	F = _____
A trapezoid has sides of 9 in., 8 in., 6 in., and 9 in. Its perimeter is **G** in.	G = _____
A triangle has a base of 7 ft. and a height of 8 ft. Its area is **H** ft.².	H = _____
A square has a perimeter of 72 in. **I** is the length of one of its sides.	I = _____
A trapezoid has sides of 8 cm, 4 cm, 8 cm, and 11 cm. Its perimeter is **J** cm.	J = _____

(E_____, A_____)   (D_____, B_____)
(8, C_____)   (12, B_____)
END OF LINE   (6, G_____)
                            (3, C_____)
(15, A_____)   (F_____, A_____)
(F_____, J_____)   (F_____, E_____)
END OF LINE   (I_____, E_____)
                            (I_____, A_____)
(A_____, A_____)   (H_____, C_____)
(D_____, 30)   (25, G_____)
END OF LINE   (D_____, B_____)
                            END OF LINE
(17, A_____)
(23, H_____)
END OF LINE

- -

Teacher: Fold under at line before photocopying.

Activity 50 Picture: Fan

A = 16	C = 29	E = 14	G = 32	I = 18
B = 33	D = 19	F = 13	H = 28	J = 31

Activity 51: Geometry

Directions: Solve each problem. Use the answers to complete the ordered pairs. Then plot the points on the graph paper. They will form a picture when connected in order.

A triangle has an area of 120 cm². Its base is 8 cm and its height is **A** cm.	A = _____
A box's volume is 78 in.³. It has sides of 2 in., 3 in., and **B** in.	B = _____
A right triangle has sides of 3 in. and 4 in. **C** is its hypotenuse.	C = _____
A rectangle has a perimeter of 54 ft. Its sides are 9 ft. and **D** ft.	D = _____
A box has sides of 2 in., 7 in., and 2 in. **E** is its volume.	E = _____
A parallelogram has an area of 32 cm². Its height is 2 cm and its base is **F** cm.	F = _____
A cube has a volume of **G** ft.³. Its sides are 3 ft.	G = _____
A trapezoid has a perimeter of 54 in. Its sides are 11 in., 14 in., 7 in. and **H** in.	H = _____
A box has sides of 2 ft., 5 ft. and 2 ft. **I** is its volume.	I = _____
An equilaterial triangle has two sides of 14 in. **J** is the length of its third side.	J = _____

(B_____, 39)
(10, 37)
(7, 31)
(6, H_____)
(8, 11)
(B_____, C_____)
(D_____, B_____)
(D_____, 29)
(F_____, 37)
(B_____, 39)
END OF LINE

(D_____, E_____)
(H_____, 26)
(H_____, F_____)
(D_____, J_____)
END OF LINE

(19, E_____)
(19, J_____)
END OF LINE

(I_____, G_____)
(I_____, 15)
END OF LINE

(7, F_____)
(C_____, C_____)
(9, C_____)
(10, 9)
END OF LINE

(D_____, B_____)
(I_____, C_____)
(F_____, C_____)
(15, 8)
END OF LINE

(B_____, J_____)
(B_____, 6)
END OF LINE

(A_____, 38)
(A_____, 1)
END OF LINE

(A_____, 36)
(G_____, 36)
(26, 33)
(G_____, A_____)
(A_____, A_____)
END OF LINE

(A_____, 35)
(E_____, 35)
(E_____, 34)
(A_____, 34)
END OF LINE

- -

Teacher: Fold under at line before photocopying.

Activity 51 Picture: Blimp

A = 30	C = 5	E = 28	G = 27	I = 20
B = 13	D = 18	F = 16	H = 22	J = 14

Activity 52: Probability

Directions: Solve each problem. Use the answers to complete the ordered pairs. Then plot the points on the graph paper. They will form a picture when connected in order.

The probability of getting a red marble from a bag of 50 is 0.36. **A** is the number of red marbles in the bag.	A = _____
B is the total of the 1s and 2s expected in 90 dice rolls.	B = _____
C is the number of heads expected in 50 coin tosses.	C = _____
The probability of an event is 19%. **D** is the number of times the event should happen in 100 trials.	D = _____
E is the number of tails expected in 32 coin tosses.	E = _____
The probability of getting a blue bead from a box of 50 is 0.26. **F** is the number of blue beads in the box.	F = _____
Mr. Wilson has 28 students in his class. He puts all their names into a box. The probability of drawing a girl's name from the box is 25%. **G** is the number of girls that are in Mr. Wilson's class.	G = _____
There is an equal number of pennies and dimes in a bag. **H** is the number of pennies expected in 62 coin draws from the bag.	H = _____
In 60 dice rolls, **I** is the total of the 3s or 4s that should appear.	I = _____
The probability of an event is 68%. In 100 trials, **J** is the number of times the event would be expected to NOT occur.	J = _____

(2, F_____)	(5, J_____)	(B_____, A_____)	(E_____, D_____)
(F_____, F_____)	(5, 34)	(B_____, I_____)	(21, A_____)
(F_____, 22)	(10, 34)	(27, C_____)	(C_____, A_____)
(8, 23)	(10, J_____)	(23, 26)	(B_____, D_____)
(8, B_____)	(8, H_____)	(D_____, C_____)	(C_____, I_____)
(11, H_____)	(G_____, H_____)	(E_____, I_____)	(21, I_____)
(11, 35)	(5, J_____)	(E_____, A_____)	(E_____, D_____)
(4, 35)	END OF LINE	END OF LINE	END OF LINE
(4, H_____)			
(G_____, B_____)	(29, A_____)	(E_____, A_____)	
(G_____, 23)	(27, G_____)	(21, 17)	
(2, 22)	(D_____, G_____)	(C_____, 17)	
(2, F_____)	(17, A_____)	(B_____, A_____)	
END OF LINE	END OF LINE	END OF LINE	

- -

Teacher: Fold under at line before photocopying.

Activity 52 Picture: Pail and Shovel

A = 18	C = 25	E = 16	G = 7	I = 20
B = 30	D = 19	F = 13	H = 31	J = 32

Activity 53: Probability

Directions: Solve each problem. Use the answers to complete the ordered pairs. Then plot the points on the graph paper. They will form a picture when connected in order.

A is the total of 5s and 6s expected in 21 dice rolls. A = _____

The probability of getting a pink lollipop from a box of 50 is 0.44. **B** is the number of pink lollipops in the box. B = _____

In 18 coin tosses, **C** is the number of heads expected. C = _____

In a game, the chance of picking a green tile is 4 out of 15 trials. There are twice as many yellow tiles as green. **D** is the chance of picking a yellow tile out of 15 trials. D = _____

The probability of an event is 5%. **E** is the number of times the event should happen in 100 trials. E = _____

F is the number of tails expected in 58 coin tosses. F = _____

Attendance at a monthly meeting is half men and half women. In January, 38 people attend the meeting. **G** is the number expected to be women. G = _____

A game spinner has the numbers 1 through 3. In 36 spins, **H** is the number of 3s expected. H = _____

The probability of pulling a black marble from a bag of 100 is 0.23. **I** is the number of black marbles in the bag. I = _____

At a carnival, 108 strawberry, chocolate, banana, and vanilla milkshake samples are given out with each flavor having the same probability. **J** is the number of banana milkshakes. J = _____

(D_____, 31)
(A_____, 30)
(A_____, I_____)
(D_____, B_____)
(G_____, B_____)
(20, I_____)
(20, 30)
(G_____, 31)
(D_____, 31)
END OF LINE

(C_____, B_____)
(10, C_____)
END OF LINE

(18, B_____)
(17, C_____)
END OF LINE

(C_____, F_____)
(H_____, F_____)
(H_____, J_____)
(C_____, J_____)
(C_____, F_____)
END OF LINE

(14, F_____)
(17, F_____)
(17, J_____)
(14, J_____)
(14, F_____)
END OF LINE

(D_____, B_____)
(D_____, H_____)
(A_____, 11)
(E_____, 11)

(4, H_____)
(4, I_____)
(E_____, 25)
(A_____, 25)
END OF LINE

(4, G_____)
(E_____, G_____)
(6, 20)
(6, B_____)
(4, B_____)
END OF LINE

(3, A_____)
(25, A_____)
END OF LINE

(A_____, I_____)
(A_____, H_____)
(E_____, H_____)
(E_____, 21)
(6, B_____)
END OF LINE

(E_____, B_____)
(E_____, I_____)
(6, 24)
(A_____, 24)
END OF LINE

(D_____, A_____)
(D_____, C_____)
(G_____, C_____)
(G_____, A_____)
END OF LINE

Teacher: Fold under at line before photocopying.

Activity 53 Picture: Gas Pump

A = 7	C = 9	E = 5	G = 19	I = 23
B = 22	D = 8	F = 29	H = 12	J = 27

Activity 54: Inequalities

Directions: Look at each set of numbers. Find the number in the set that satisfies the inequality. Use the answers to complete the ordered pairs. Then plot the points on the graph paper. They will form a picture when connected in order.

(4, 5, 7, 9)	A > 7	A = _____
(9, 10, 12, 14)	B < 14 and B > 10	B = _____
(6, 7, 9, 11)	C > 9	C = _____
(9, 10, 12, 14)	D > 12	D = _____
(13, 15, 17, 18)	E < 15	E = _____
(2, 3, 5, 7)	F < 7 and F > 3	F = _____
(5, 6, 8, 10)	G < 10 and G > 6	G = _____
(⁻1, 0, 2, 4)	H > 2	H = _____
(⁻17, ⁻15, ⁻13, ⁻12)	I < ⁻15	I = _____
(10, 12, 14, 15)	J < 12	J = _____

(2, ⁻6)	(A_____, 1)	(D_____, C_____)	(H_____, ⁻10)
(7, I_____)	(A_____, F_____)	(D_____, D_____)	(2, ⁻14)
(E_____, I_____)	(E_____, 6)	(B_____, 17)	(6, I_____)
(C_____, ⁻16)	(D_____, A_____)	(A_____, 18)	(H_____, ⁻16)
(E_____, ⁻16)	(E_____, G_____)	(F_____, 17)	(F_____, I_____)
(C_____, ⁻15)	(E_____, A_____)	(H_____, D_____)	(3, ⁻16)
(E_____, ⁻14)	(B_____, G_____)	(H_____, A_____)	(H_____, I_____)
(A_____, ⁻15)	(B_____, A_____)	(⁻4, ⁻8)	(⁻2, ⁻15)
(6, ⁻7)	(C_____, G_____)	(⁻13, ⁻14)	(1, ⁻9)
(A_____, ⁻1)	(C_____, A_____)	(⁻4, ⁻12)	END OF LINE
END OF LINE	(J_____, G_____)	(3, ⁻8)	
	(A_____, J_____)	END OF LINE	
(F_____, ⁻2)	(J_____, B_____)		
(D_____, 0)	(C_____, C_____)	(A_____, 16)	
(B_____, 0)	(C_____, B_____)	(G_____, 15)	
(D_____, 1)	(B_____, C_____)	(A_____, D_____)	
(F_____, 1)	(B_____, B_____)	(J_____, 15)	
(F_____, ⁻2)	(E_____, C_____)	(A_____, 16)	
END OF LINE	(E_____, B_____)	END OF LINE	

- -

Teacher: Fold under at line before photocopying.

Activity 54 Picture: T-Rex

A = 9	C = 11	E = 13	G = 8	I = ⁻17
B = 12	D = 14	F = 5	H = 4	J = 10

Activity 55: Word Problems

Directions: Solve each word problem. Use the answers to complete the ordered pairs. Then plot the points on the graph paper. They will form a picture when connected in order.

This week Tom worked for 1,140 minutes. **A** is the number of hours that Tom worked.	A = _____
A bicyclist travels 6.5 miles in a half hour. **B** is the number of miles the bicyclist travels in one hour.	B = _____
Kim started to nap at 1:15 P.M. and woke at 1:44 P.M. **C** is the number of minutes she napped.	C = _____
A train goes 25 miles per hour. **D** is the number of hours it needs to go 125 miles.	D = _____
A limousine gets 8 miles per gallon of gas. **E** is the number of miles it can go on 3 gallons.	E = _____
A cheetah runs 11 meters per second. **F** is the number of meters it runs in 2 seconds.	F = _____
A triangle has interior angles of 87°, 66°, and **G**°.	G = _____
A bus goes 400 miles on 25 gallons of gas. **H** is the bus's miles per gallon.	H = _____
A wheel with a circumference of 3 inches is rotating at 5 rotations per minute. **I** is the distance the wheel travels in one minute.	I = _____
A 4-sided shape has interior angles of 71°, 200°, 77°, and **J**°.	J = _____

(I_____, G_____)	(H_____, E_____)	(A_____, 31)	(B_____, J_____)
(C_____, G_____)	(H_____, 39)	(23, G_____)	(I_____, J_____)
(C_____, E_____)	(A_____, 39)	END OF LINE	(I_____, 9)
(A_____, E_____)	(A_____, C_____)		(B_____, 9)
(18, 26)	(17, 28)	(23, E_____)	(B_____, J_____)
(4, 26)	(17, B_____)	(25, D_____)	END OF LINE
(4, C_____)	(14, B_____)	END OF LINE	
(14, C_____)	(14, 23)		(18, D_____)
(I_____, G_____)	(H_____, E_____)	(4, D_____)	(18, B_____)
END OF LINE	END OF LINE	(30, D_____)	(F_____, B_____)
		END OF LINE	(F_____, D_____)
	(9, D_____)		END OF LINE
	(11, 26)	(A_____, F_____)	
	END OF LINE	(21, F_____)	(A_____, 10)
		(21, A_____)	(A_____, 9)
	(J_____, C_____)	(A_____, A_____)	END OF LINE
	(H_____, 32)	(A_____, F_____)	
	END OF LINE	END OF LINE	

- -

Teacher: Fold under at line before photocopying.

Activity 55 Picture: Windmill

A = 19	C = 29	E = 24	G = 27	I = 15
B = 13	D = 5	F = 22	H = 16	J = 12

Activity 56: Word Problems

Directions: Solve each word problem. Use the answers to complete the ordered pairs. Then plot the points on the graph paper. They will form a picture when connected in order.

A triangle has interior angles of 101°, 65°, and **A**°.	A = _____
A car gets 25 miles per gallon. **B** is the number of gallons it needs to travel 600 miles.	B = _____
An SUV goes 330 miles on 15 gallons of gas. **C** is the number of miles per gallon the SUV gets.	C = _____
Sarah worked for 1,200 minutes this week. **D** is the number of hours she worked.	D = _____
Nathan got to the bus stop at 10:15 A.M. The bus came at 10:52 A.M. **E** is the number of minutes that he waited for the bus.	E = _____
Robert made a $77 purchase. He paid with a $100 bill. **F** is the amount of change he received.	F = _____
Erin got $50 for her birthday. She has already spent $31. **G** is the amount of money she has left.	G = _____
A man walks 3 kilometers per hour. **H** is the number of kilometers he walks in 6 hours.	H = _____
Laura is **I** years old. In another 43 years she will turn 60.	I = _____
Jack is having a party. He has 14 guests and 168 pieces of candy. He distributes the same amount of candy to each guest. **J** is the number of pieces of candy each guest gets.	J = _____

(10, E_____)	(25, 30)	(D_____, D_____)	(J_____, I_____)
(8, 34)	(B_____, 34)	(27, C_____)	(5, H_____)
(7, 30)	(C_____, E_____)	(31, G_____)	(1, A_____)
(10, F_____)	END OF LINE	END OF LINE	END OF LINE
(J_____, C_____)			
(11, I_____)	(A_____, B_____)	(D_____, I_____)	(13, A_____)
(13, J_____)	(A_____, F_____)	(27, H_____)	(5, A_____)
(J_____, 9)	(15, F_____)	(31, A_____)	(1, 11)
(13, 6)	(A_____, B_____)	END OF LINE	END OF LINE
(11, 3)	END OF LINE		
(15, 2)		(G_____, A_____)	(C_____, E_____)
(16, 3)	(H_____, B_____)	(27, A_____)	(21, 29)
(I_____, 2)	(H_____, F_____)	(31, 11)	(D_____, E_____)
(21, 3)	(I_____, F_____)	END OF LINE	(H_____, 30)
(G_____, 6)	(H_____, B_____)		(G_____, B_____)
(D_____, 9)	END OF LINE	(J_____, D_____)	(13, B_____)
(G_____, J_____)		(5, C_____)	(A_____, 29)
(21, I_____)		(1, G_____)	(11, E_____)
(D_____, C_____)		END OF LINE	(11, 29)
(C_____, F_____)			(10, E_____)
			END OF LINE

- -

Teacher: Fold under at line before photocopying.

Activity 56 Picture: Crayfish

A = 14	C = 22	E = 37	G = 19	I = 17
B = 24	D = 20	F = 23	H = 18	J = 12

Graph Paper A

Name: _____ **Activity:** _____ **Page:** _____

Name: _____ **Activity:** _____ **Page:** _____

Activity 1: Star, page 9

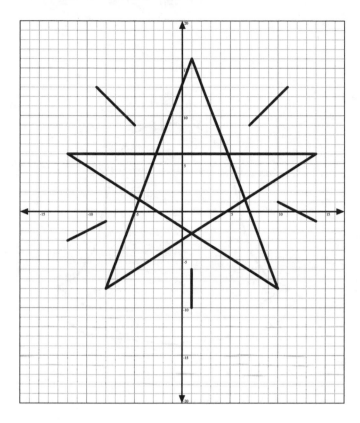

Activity 3: Rocket, page 11

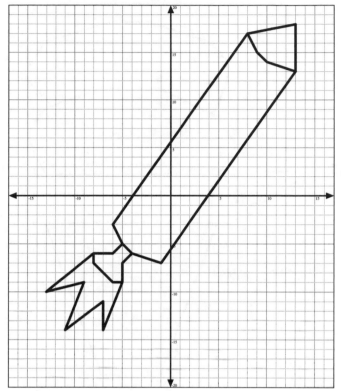

Activity 2: Swan, page 10

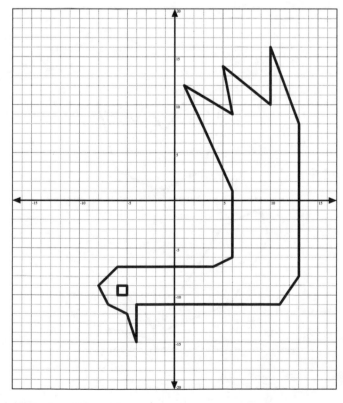

Activity 4: Mailbox, page 12

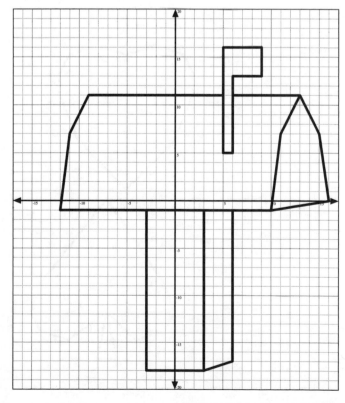

Activity 5: Ice Cream Cone, page 13

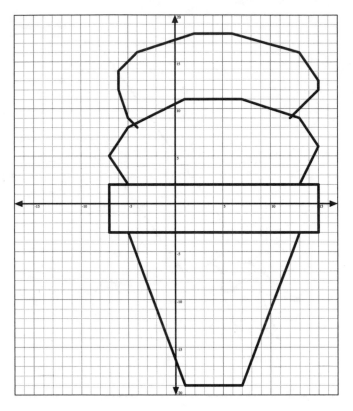

Activity 7: Bell, page 15

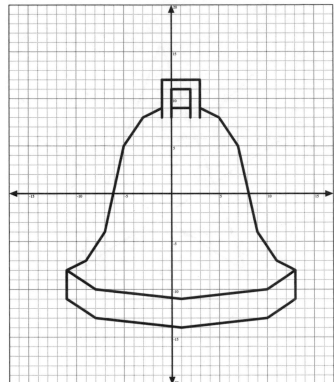

Activity 6: Heart and Spade, page 14

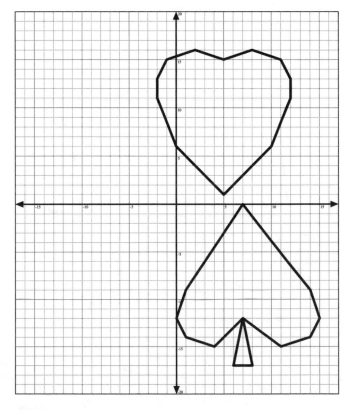

Activity 8: Tulip, page 16

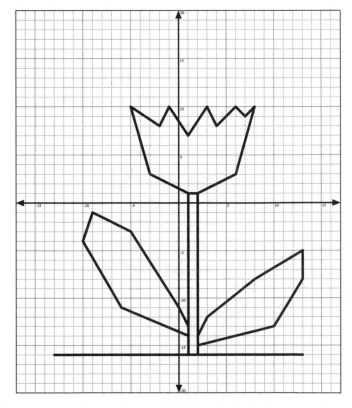

Activity 9: Flamingo, page 17

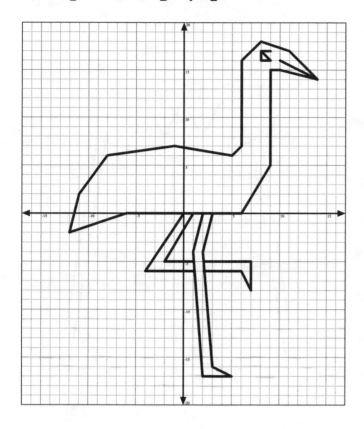

Activity 11: Club and Diamond, page 19

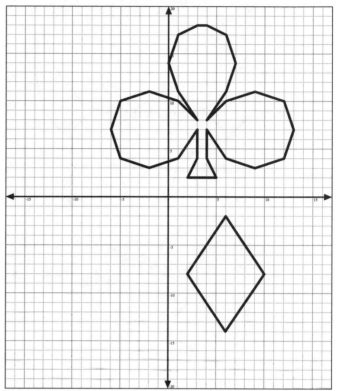

Activity 10: Fish, page 18

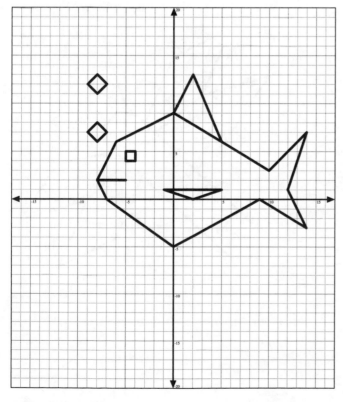

Activity 12: Kangaroo, page 20

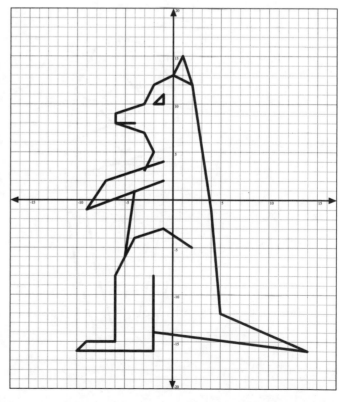

Activity 13: Cattle Skull, page 21

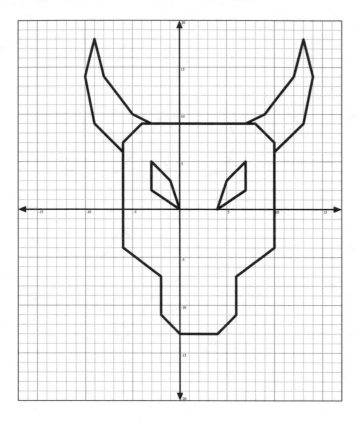

Activity 15: Water Tower, page 23

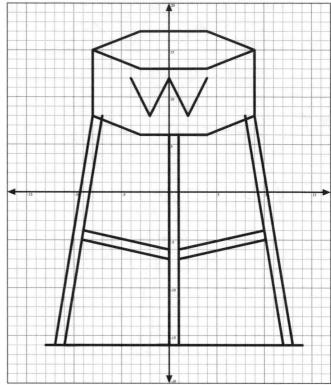

Activity 14: Pliers, page 22

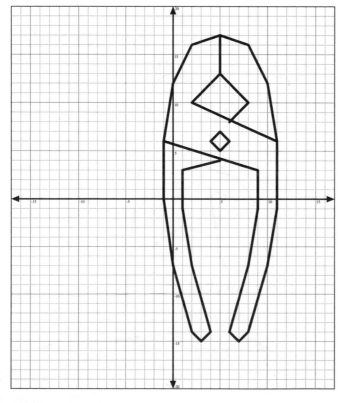

Activity 16: Dragonfly, page 24

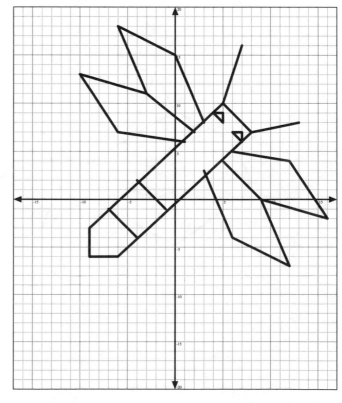

Activity 17: Brontosaurus, page 25

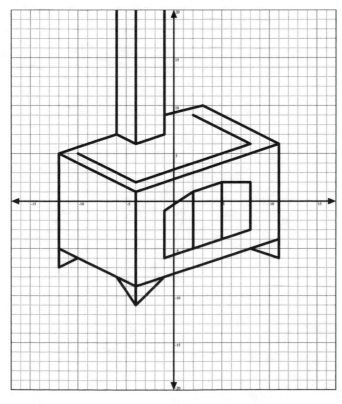

Activity 19: Butterfly, page 27

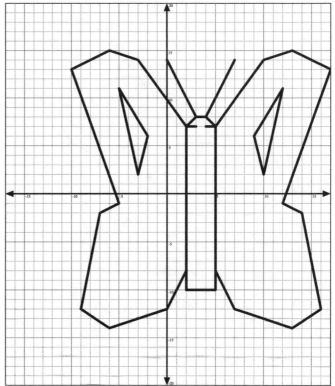

Activity 18: Wood Stove, page 26

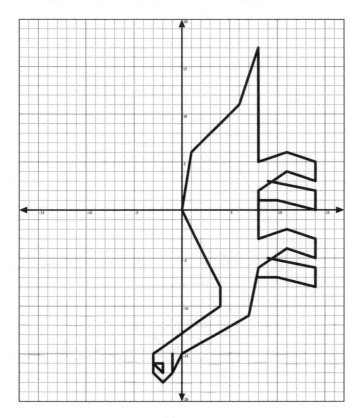

Activity 20: Elephant, page 28

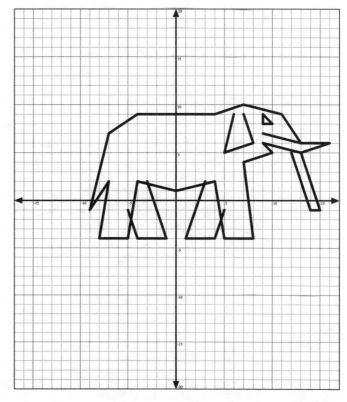

Activity 21: Rattlesnake, page 29

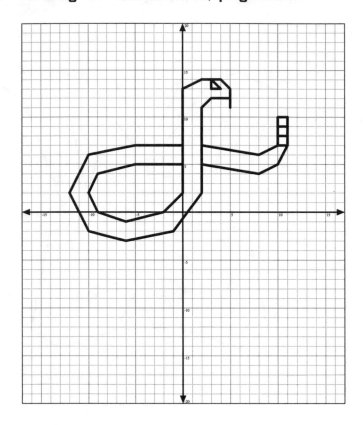

Activity 23: Barn, page 31

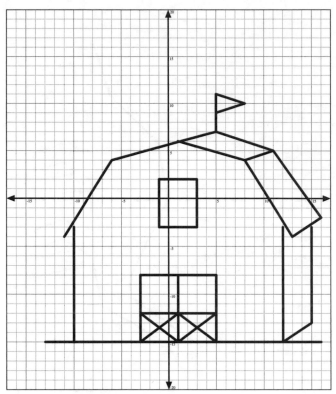

Activity 22: Plane, page 30

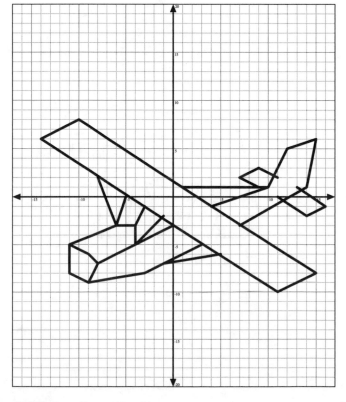

Activity 24: Turtle, page 32

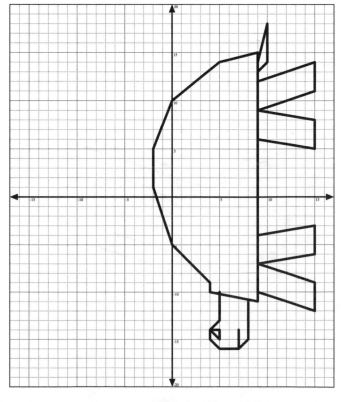

Activity 25: Tractor, page 33

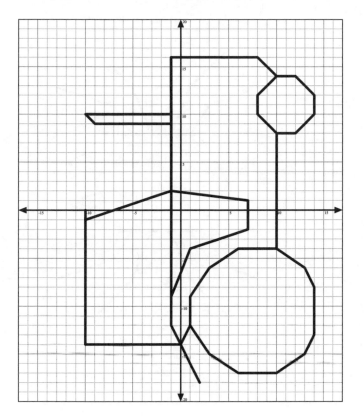

Activity 27: Helicopter, page 35

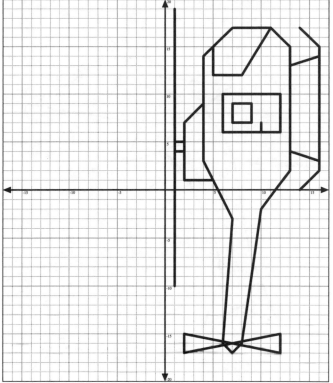

Activity 26: Tent, page 34

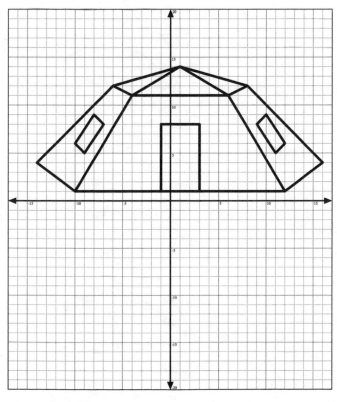

Activity 28: Giraffe, page 36

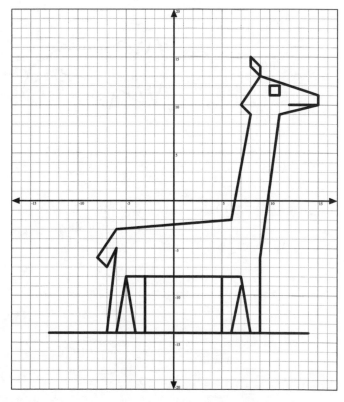

Activity 29: Dolphin, page 37

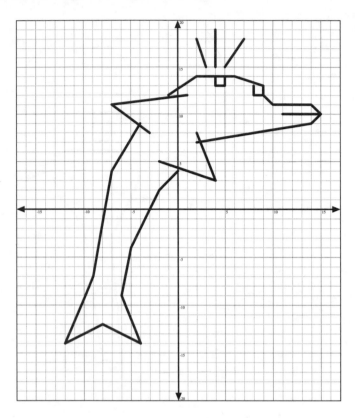

Activity 31: Spider, page 39

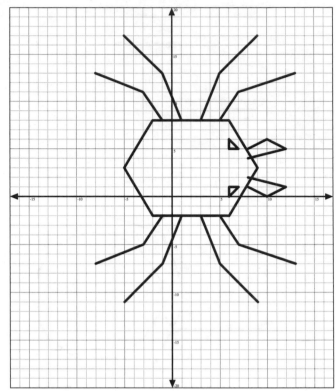

Activity 30: Hammer, page 38

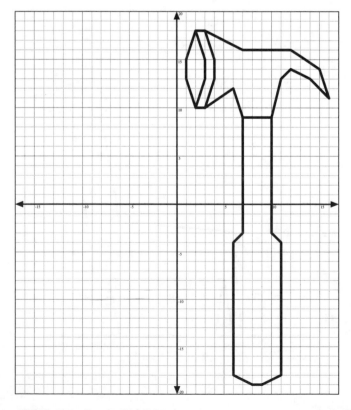

Activity 32: Fishing Trawler, page 40

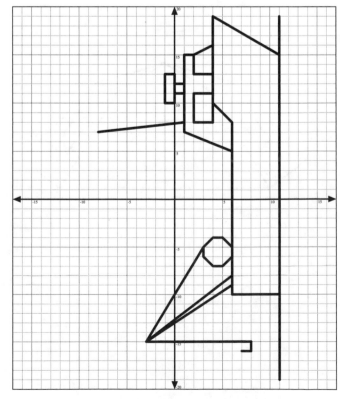

Activity 33: Salamander, page 41

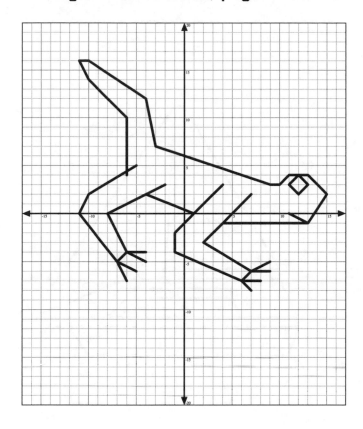

Activity 35: Penguin, page 43

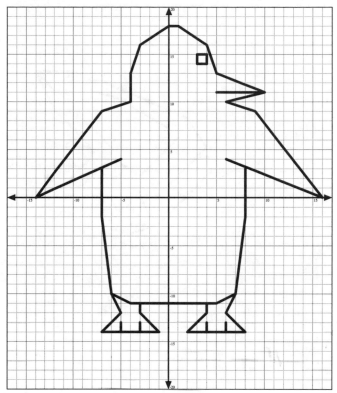

Activity 34: Canoe, page 42

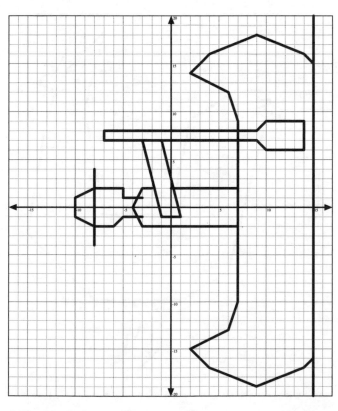

Activity 36: Ant, page 44

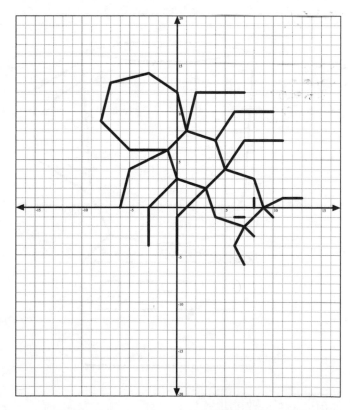

Activity 37: Frog, page 45

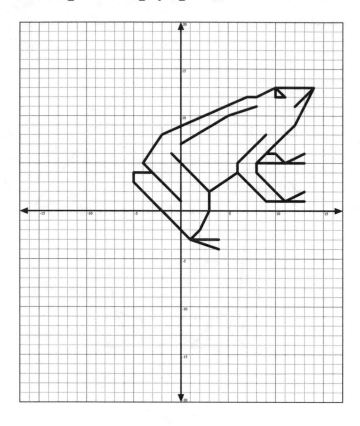

Activity 39: Sailboat, page 47

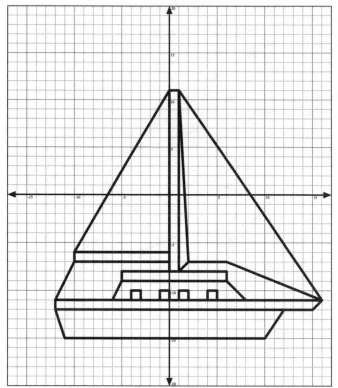

Activity 38: Blender, page 46

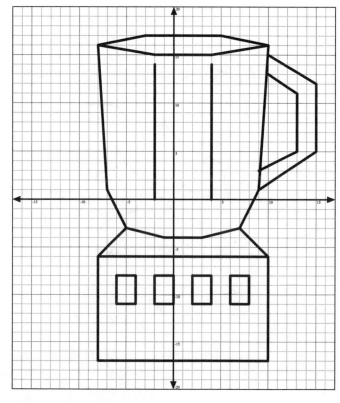

Activity 40: Rooster, page 48

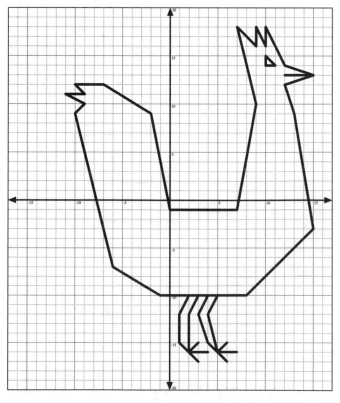

Activity 41: Space Shuttle, page 49

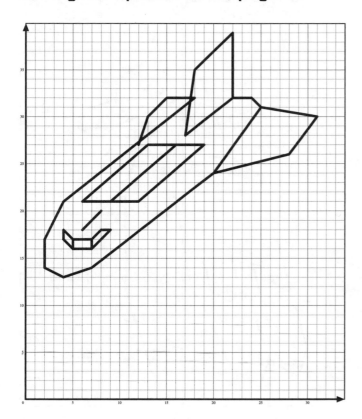

Activity 43: Candle, page 51

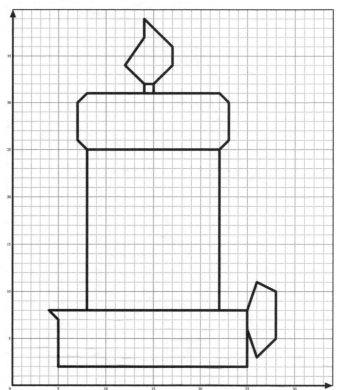

Activity 42: Kite, page 50

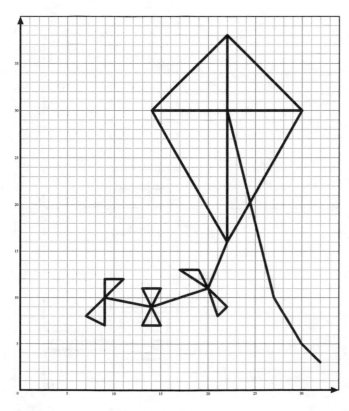

Activity 44: Squirrel, page 52

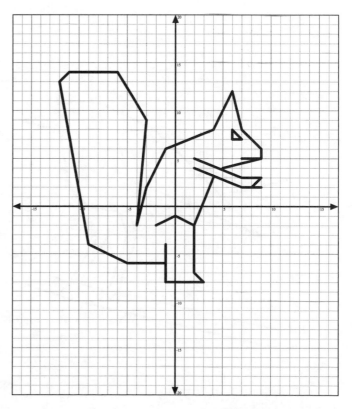

Activity 45: Power Shovel, page 53

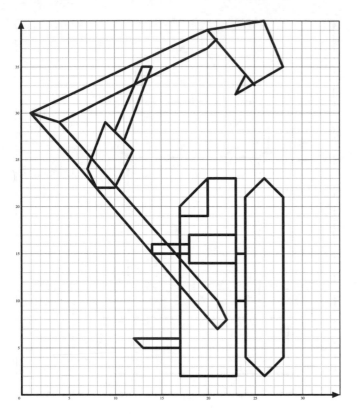

Activity 47: Eagle, page 55

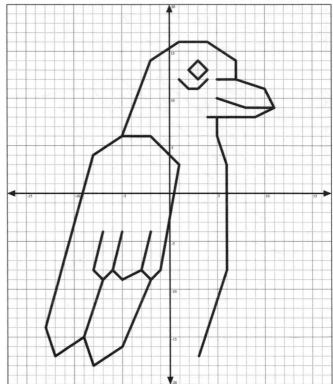

Activity 46: Robin, page 54

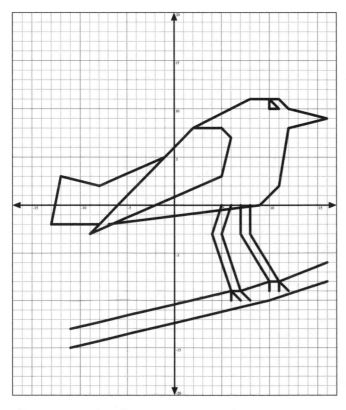

Activity 48: Motorboat, page 56

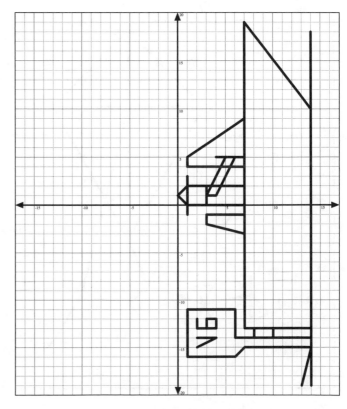

Activity 49: Bat, page 57

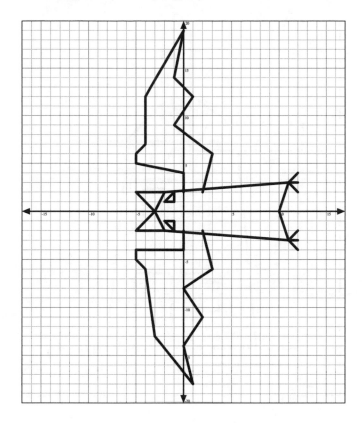

Activity 51: Blimp, page 59

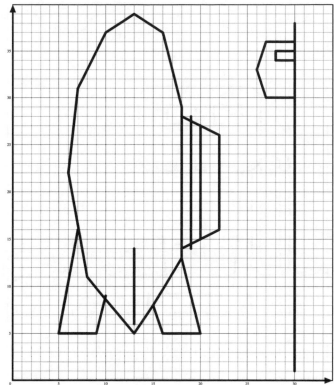

Activity 50: Fan, page 58

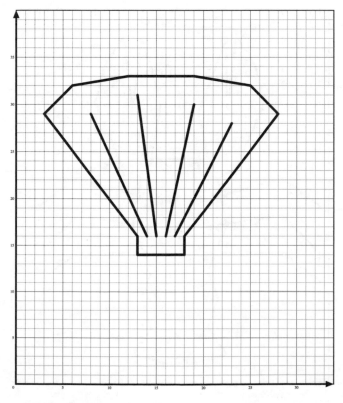

Activity 52: Pail and Shovel, page 60

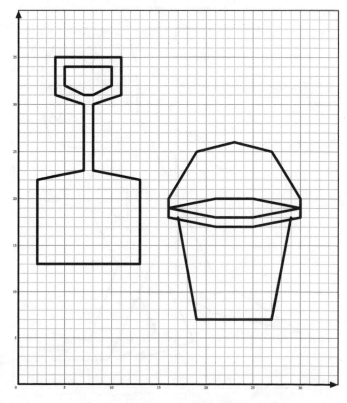

Solutions

Activity 53: Gas Pump, page 61

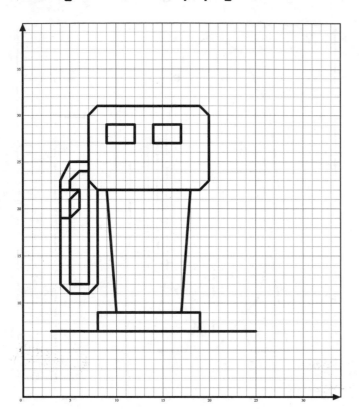

Activity 55: Windmill, page 63

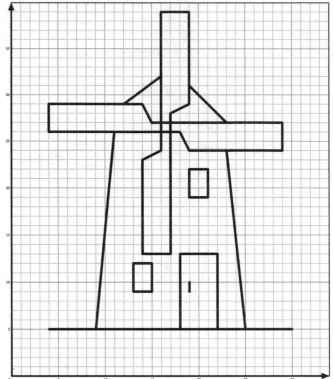

Activity 54: T-Rex, page 62

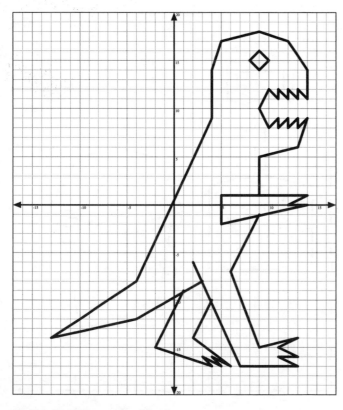

Activity 56: Crayfish, page 64

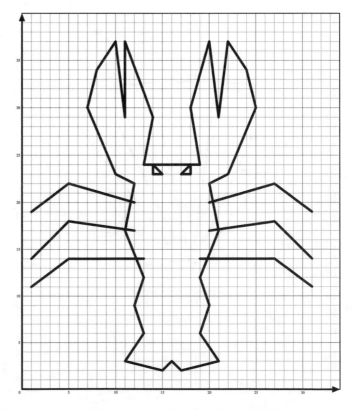